BEYOND HIDDEN DANGERS

Railway Safety into the 21st Century

Stanley Hall

Ian Allan PUBLISHING

Front cover:
The wreckage of the 04.40 GNER express from Newcastle to King's Cross after it became derailed following a collision with a land rover vehicle and ran into a head-on collision with a coal train.
Rail magazine/Philip Haigh

Back cover upper:
Track torn up at Hatfield after the 12.10 GNER express from King's Cross to Leeds became derailed by a broken rail.
Rail magazine/Philip Haigh

Back cover lower:
A graphic picture of the crash at Southall when the 10.32 GWT HST from Swansea to Paddington collided with an empty wagon train. *Rail magazine/Philip Haigh*

Previous page:
Southall on the morning following the collision on 19 September 1997.
Ken Brunt

Left:
The crumpled Class 142 diesel railcar after being run into by a Class 87 electric locomotive near Winsford on 23 June 1999. *A. J. Miles*

First published 2003

ISBN 0 7110 2915 6

Published by Ian Allan Publishing

an imprint of Ian Allan Publishing Ltd, Hersham, Surrey KT12 4RG.
Printed by Ian Allan Printing Ltd, Hersham, Surrey KT12 4RG.

Code: 0304/B1

Contents

Preface

THIS book examines the present state of safety on Britain's railways and continues the story from the author's previous volume *Hidden Dangers*, published by Ian Allan Publishing in 1999. Inevitably, there is a certain amount of overlap between the two books, particularly in the case of the Southall accident, but the official report of the judicial inquiry into that accident had not been published in time to be included in the previous volume, and it raises many important issues. In addition, further information has become available concerning some of the accidents discussed in that book.

In the last four years there have been a number of serious accidents — at Ladbroke Grove, Hatfield, Great Heck and Potters Bar — and they have given rise to several wide-ranging judicial inquiries held in public. In fact, it would be true to say that never before in railway history has there been such an outpouring of inquiry reports into accidents and train protection systems, containing in total well over a thousand pages, several hundred recommendations and much food for thought.

Four years ago, Railtrack shares stood at £13.00. In 2001 they had sunk to below £3.00 and the then Secretary of State, Stephen Byers, somewhat peremptorily placed Railtrack into administration by court order. He lost his job by doing so. A new undertaking, a 'not for dividend' company, limited by government guarantee and called Network Rail, has been created from the ashes of Railtrack, but its powers have been severely reduced by the transfer of some of them to the Strategic Rail Authority (SRA). The order which placed Railtrack PLC into administration was lifted on 1 October 2002, which enabled the company to be sold to Network Rail on 3 October 2002. The chairman of the company is Ian McAllister, formerly the head of car manufacturer Ford UK. In this book I have used the terms Railtrack and Network Rail in their historically correct setting, where possible.

During our review period the SRA has been statutorily established under Richard Bowker, and has rapidly taken unto itself many of the powers, strategic and otherwise, which resided in the industry. In effect, both Network Rail and the Train Operating Companies are becoming responsible only for day-to-day operations. The SRA will determine questions of track occupancy, the terms and conditions of the franchises of Train Operators, and infrastructure enhancements, obtaining funding from the Treasury for the latter. At the time of writing, the industry is still in a state of flux, and the question of what, if anything, ought to be done will be reviewed in the final chapter.

During our four-year period, the issue that has provoked most heat, and perhaps least light, has been Automatic Train Protection (ATP). Following Southall and Ladbroke Grove, ATP was considered by some to be the *sine qua non* of railway train control systems and there were calls for it to be installed at once, but calmer reflection has produced a realisation both of the very considerable cost and the less than considerable benefits of ATP. That calmer reflection has been helped by the fact that none of the three serious accidents since Ladbroke Grove could have been prevented by ATP. And it cannot be emphasised too strongly that the simpler AWS (Automatic Warning System) on its own could have prevented the Southall collision, but no system is of any value when it is switched off, as happened on that occasion.

The once optimistic view that ATP was ready to be installed off the shelf has been replaced by a more sober realisation that modern ATP is technically very advanced and may not be available in quantity production in its more advanced forms for some years. ATP has become part of the European Train Control System (ETCS), itself part of the European Rail Traffic

Management System (ERTMS). I apologise for all the sets of initials. They have always been part of railway life but they seem to have proliferated since privatisation.

I have been fortunate during the last four years to have had the opportunity to continue making a thorough study of railway safety and the underlying causes of accidents, and to attend public inquiries. I have also been helped by discussions with colleagues and through the activities of the Institution of Railway Signal Engineers and the Institution of Railway Operators. I am very grateful to all those who have helped me with information, ideas and their own views, but I would particularly like to thank Roy Bell OBE, a very senior signal engineer, and Peter van der Mark, a very knowledgeable and experienced HST driver with Great Western Trains, for all their help, both with information and advice and for their comments on the draft manuscript.

I would not like the reader to gain the impression that I have no feelings of sympathy or sorrow for those bereaved or grievously injured. On the contrary, I feel very sad when the railway I served for 40 years has a serious accident. It is a personal thing which many railwaymen share, but it also has to be recognised that emotion has no place in a critical examination of railway accidents, their causes, and the actions that might be taken to prevent a recurrence. All railwaymen desire a safer railway, but they know from hard experience that funds are not unlimited and that even safety has its price, harsh though that may sound.

Now that I have written this book, I have come to the conclusion that the industry stands at a crossroads, and that it will not succeed without radical change. I appreciate that this is not a popular view, and that people in the industry want a period of stability, but I am convinced that there needs to be at the very least a reduction in the number of interfaces and an increase in integration. Not renationalisation, though. But the problem with any railway organisation will be the funding of it. That is the nub.

Stanley Hall
Honorary Fellow, Institution of Railway Signal Engineers
Fellow, Institution of Railway Operators
Chartered Member, Institute of Logistics and Transport
March 2003

List of abbreviations

ARS	Automatic Route Setting	HSE	Health & Safety Executive
ASLEF	Associated Society of Locomotive Engineers & Firemen	HST	High Speed Train (a specific type of train, otherwise known as InterCity 125)
ATC	Automatic Train Control	IECC	Integrated Electronic Control Centre
ATOC	Association of Train Operating Companies	LED	Light Emitting Diode
ATP	Automatic Train Protection	LGRI	Ladbroke Grove Rail Inquiry
AWS	Automatic Warning System (of Train Control)	LMS(R)	London, Midland & Scottish (Railway)
BR	British Railways	LNER	London & North Eastern Railway
BRB	British Railways Board	NRN	National Radio Network
BTP	British Transport Police	OHLE	Overhead Line Equipment
CSR	Cab Secure Radio	ORR	Office of the Rail Regulator
DOO(P)	Driver-Only Operated train (passenger)	RAIB	Railway Accidents Investigation Branch
DSD	Driver's Safety Device	RI	Railway Inspectorate
DVD	Driver's Vigilance Device	RISB	Railway Industry Safety Board
ERTMS	European Rail Traffic Management System	RMT	(National Union of) Rail, Maritime & Transport
ETCS	European Train Control System	S&SD	Safety & Standards Directorate
EWS	English, Welsh & Scottish Railway (freight company)	SPAD	Signal Passed at Danger
GNER	Great North Eastern Railway	SRA	Strategic Rail Authority
GSM-R	Global System for Mobile Communication — Railways	TOC	Train Operating Company
GWT	Great Western Trains	TPWS	Train Protection & Warning System
HMRI	Her Majesty's Railway Inspectorate	TSI	Technical Specification for Interoperability
HSC	Health & Safety Commission	VDU	Visual Display Unit

❶ The state of railway safety at privatisation

How good was it?

It is surprisingly difficult to fix the effective date of railway privatisation. The Act that provided for privatisation was the Railways Act 1993, which came into force on 5 November 1993, but the process of selling off various parts of the railway and franchising the operation of train services occupied several years. The government had decided that the infrastructure should belong to a separate company, subsequently called Railtrack. Under the Act it was split off from British Railways in April 1994, but remained in public ownership *pro tem* as a nationalised industry. Railtrack was sold off in April 1996 and became a PLC. Franchising the passenger services began in February 1996 and continued throughout the year.

It is evident, therefore, that selecting a date on which privatisation became effective can only be arbitrary, but by the end of 1996 the process was almost complete, and the date of 31 December 1996 has been chosen for the purposes of this chapter.

It might have been expected that the standards of railway safety which were actually achieved during the 1990s up to 1996 would have been adversely affected by the comprehensive upheaval of the privatisation process and the destruction of British Rail's highly effective safety organisation, but this was far from the case. Indeed, those seven years (1990-6) were the safest in railway history so far as passengers' deaths in train accidents were concerned. There were only five train accidents in which passengers were killed, and there were only eight passenger fatalities. Indeed, there was a continuous period of 1,181 days between 21 July 1991 and 15 October 1994 during which there was not a single passenger fatality in a train accident. This was an achievement without parallel in the history of the railways of Britain, both before and since.

This chapter, indeed this book, is concerned with the safe operation of the railway, and it would be instructive to examine the circumstances of the five accidents that did occur in this period.

London Cannon Street (Southern Region) 8 January 1991

The 07.58 suburban passenger train from Sevenoaks to London Cannon Street station consisted of three electric multiple-units of Mk 1 stock with a total of 10 coaches. It picked up passengers at several stations *en route*, and by the time it left London Bridge station, its last stop before Cannon Street, it was carrying around 900 passengers. The front half of the train was crowded, with over 100 passengers standing, but there were almost 200 empty seats in the rear half. Most of the standing passengers had joined the train only at London Bridge and preferred to stand near the front of the train for the short journey so that they could make a quick getaway at Cannon Street. The train ran into Cannon Street station as normal but as it approached the buffer stops it did not slow down and collided with them at about 10mph. Even at that comparatively low speed a train weighing several hundred tonnes has a considerable amount of kinetic energy and there was slight telescoping between two of the coaches in the middle of the train, causing the deaths of two passengers.

Newton (Glasgow, Scottish Region) 21 July 1991

Newton is a suburban station to the southeast of Glasgow and the turnround point of some suburban services. The 21.55 from Newton to Glasgow, a three-car Class 303 electric multiple-unit, started away from the platform and passed the signal at the end of the platform at Danger. It collided head-on with an incoming train, the 20.55 from Balloch to Motherwell (a three-car Class 314 electric multiple-unit), at a closing speed estimated to be about 60mph. As it was a Sunday evening both trains were very lightly loaded, and only two passengers were killed. Both drivers were killed also.

Cowden (between Oxted and Uckfield, Southern Region) 15 October 1994

Saturday 15 October 1994 was a typical autumn morning with drifting mist. The driver of the 08.00 train from Uckfield to Oxted ran past a colour-light signal showing red and on to a section of single line. Near Cowden station the train ran into a head-on collision with the 08.04 train from Oxted to Uckfield which was just starting away from that station, at a closing speed in the region of 60mph. Both trains were very lightly loaded and there were only 15 passengers in total in the two trains. Both drivers were killed, together with a guard and two passengers in the train from Uckfield.

Maidenhead (Western Region) 8 September 1995

A westbound High Speed Train (HST) from Paddington was approaching Maidenhead at full speed when one of the diesel fuel tanks on the leading power car became partially detached and ruptured as it impacted against the track. Spilt diesel fuel ignited and the flames ran along the outside of the front part of the train. By the time the train stopped, the fire had practically burnt itself out, but a passenger was killed when he jumped from the stationary train into the path of another train on an adjacent track. It was concluded that the nuts on the rear bolts that secured the fuel tank had become loose and then unscrewed themselves completely owing to the vibration of the power car. This allowed the rear of the tank to drop on to the track.

Watford South Junction (London Midland Region) 8 August 1996

The 17.04 electric multiple-unit from Euston to Milton Keynes was approaching Watford Junction station when the driver passed a signal at red and collided with an empty stock train crossing its path. One passenger was killed, being thrown through the carriage window by the force of the impact. The signal at red, No WJ759, had been preceded by a yellow signal at WJ755 and a double yellow signal at WJ751 in the normal manner.

What were the fundamental causes of these accidents?

Cannon Street

It was not possible to determine why the train ran into the buffers. Nothing was found in the condition of the train or the track that could have caused the accident, and the Inspecting Officer who held the public inquiry was unable to reach a

The scene at London's Cannon Street station on 8 January 1991 after the 07.58 suburban commuter train from Sevenoaks had crashed into the buffer stops at about 10mph. Some telescoping took place near the middle of the train and two passengers were killed. *The Times*

conclusion other than to say that he concluded that the driver had failed to make a proper brake application and was thus responsible for the accident.

The 24-year-old driver had been appointed two and a half years earlier. He was examined by the Southern Region's medical adviser after the accident, who formed the opinion that the driver was unfit for driving duties. A urine analysis for drug abuse had found traces of cannabinoid products, and this indicated that it would have been relevant (ie it was present in the driver's body) at the time of the accident. It was against the British Railways' Rules to report for duty under the influence of any drug that might impair the proper performance of duty.

Since that date, driver selection and training procedures have become more thorough, and there is now a much more positive attitude against the use of drink or drugs before taking duty. However, changes in such attitudes are guided by, and reflect, current public opinion to some extent and occur only gradually. The British Railways Board was in the forefront of action against what is now known as drug or alcohol abuse.

The great majority of buffer stop collisions occur at very low speed (41 were recorded in 1990, but only eight in 2000/1), and the Cannon Street accident was the first instance in the last 30 years of passengers being killed. The two passengers were killed when slight telescoping occurred between the fifth and sixth coaches.

The coaches were of Mk 1 construction, and were the standard type constructed by British Railways during the 1950s and 1960s. They have an excellent safety record but that did not prevent the Health & Safety Executive from deciding later that all Mk 1 coaches must be withdrawn from

Above:
A Southern Region Class 415/4 electric multiple-unit passes South Croydon on 2 June 1982. A four-car set of this type formed the centre portion of the train which crashed into the buffers at Cannon Street. *Alex Dasi-Sutton*

Left:
A Southern Region Class 416/2 electric multiple-unit arrives at Waterloo East on 6 July 1979 forming the 17.22 from Charing Cross to Dartford. A two-car unit of this type formed the last two coaches of the train which crashed into the buffers at Cannon Street. *Brian Morrison*

service on safety grounds by the year 2007, subsequently brought forward to 1 January 2005. There was no real justification for this peremptory decision, taken in haste and without proper consideration, and until there is another buffer stop collision in identical circumstances with more modern stock it is not possible to judge how well-founded it was. Such a circumstance is highly unlikely; identical circumstances rarely occur. It is probable that the HSE's decision was based in part upon the consequences of the Clapham collision in which Mk 1 coaches suffered severe damage, but it is not possible to say that more modern coaches would have fared any better in those particular circumstances. The Ladbroke Grove accident lends no support to a view that they would have done, although that evidence was not available to the HSE at the time.

However, there is another consideration. Mk 1 coaches have slam doors, and whilst these are excellent for spreading the load of passengers along a coach and for allowing quick loading and unloading at stations, they are the cause of a number of fatal accidents each year. Those accidents occur when passengers attempt to join moving trains and when they fall out of them. Modern coaches, with power-operated doors under traincrew control, avoid these accidents and allow more punctual departures from stations. It could be argued that the Southern Region should have adopted sliding doors after World War 2, as happened on both the Eastern and Scottish regions, but strongly entrenched regional attitudes prevailed. It is a matter for debate as to whether the British Railways Board and its predecessors should have enforced a common policy on this issue. Incidentally, the fitting of secondary door locking to slam door stock used on main line services has led to a dramatic reduction in the number of deaths caused by passengers falling out of moving trains. There were only three such cases in 2001/2. It has also been of considerable benefit in assisting the safe and efficient despatch of trains from stations. The credit for the concept of secondary door locking belongs to the HSE, which made it a requirement.

Newton

The track layout at Newton had recently been changed to allow for higher speed running on the West Coast main line. It had the effect of introducing on the adjacent suburban line small sections of single line used by trains in both directions, with the attendant risk of head-on collision if a driver were to pass a signal at Danger.

Instances of drivers passing signals at Danger located at the end of station platforms, after stopping at the station for passenger purposes, have been endemic, resulting in several fatal collisions. It had always been assumed that the sending of the 'Train ready to start' bell signal from the guard to the driver had the propensity to act psychologically on the driver's mind and cause him to overlook the signal at Danger, but the train concerned in passing a red signal at Newton was being worked without a guard under the 'Driver-only operation' arrangements. However, the potential distraction from observing the signal, caused by giving attention to platform work, closing the doors and timekeeping, does introduce an additional hazard.

There were several theories as to what might have caused the driver to pass the starting signal at Danger. In one, it was suggested that the incoming train from Balloch had been stopped at a signal on the approach to Newton station because the signalman had cleared the platform starting signal at Newton when the empty train had run into the platform from the turnback siding a few minutes earlier. The theory then suggests that the signalman realised that the train from Balloch was approaching and therefore restored the platform starting signal to Danger to give the train from Balloch priority over the common piece of single line into the station. In such circumstances the cancellation of a route caused by restoring a signal to Danger does not occur

Collision at Newton (ScR), 21 July 1991, showing the layout at the time of the accident.

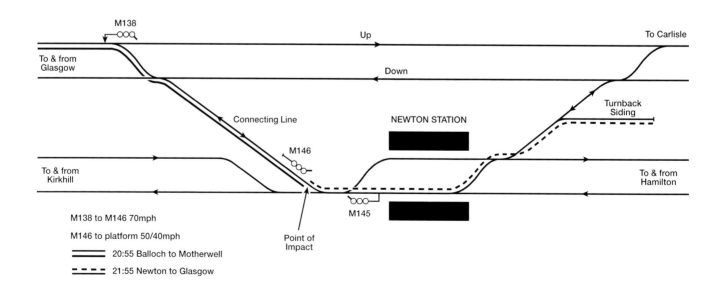

M138 to M146 70mph

M146 to platform 50/40mph

20:55 Balloch to Motherwell

21:55 Newton to Glasgow

Above:
A Scottish Region Class 303 electric multiple-unit leaves Motherwell with the 11.26 from Lanark to Milngavie on 10 September 1981. A unit of this class formed the 21.55 from Newton to Glasgow on 21 July 1991 and was involved in the head-on collision at Newton that evening. *Les Bertram*

Below:
Two electric multiple-units, a Class 303 and a Class 314, await their next turn of duty at Motherwell on 22 March 1988. These were the types involved in the Newton accident on 21 July 1991. The Class 303s were the original Glasgow 'Blue Trains' and were first introduced in 1959. The Class 314s were relatively modern by comparison, being built at York and introduced into service in 1979. *A. O. Wynn*

A Class 207 diesel-electric multiple-unit is seen standing at Ashurst station on 5 September 1987 with the 09.42 from Uckfield to Victoria. Units of a similar type (Class 205) were involved in the head-on collision near Cowden on 15 October 1994. *Alex Dasi-Sutton*

immediately but incurs a two-minute 'timing-out' penalty, during which time the train from Balloch actually came to a stand. If that is what actually happened, it would be evident that the driver of the train which started at Newton did not notice the change of signal aspect from 'Clear' to 'Danger', but he should have rechecked the signal before starting away. However, it should be noted that the Rules require that if such an aspect change is made, the driver affected must be informed by the signalman before the signals for any conflicting move are cleared. No evidence was given on that issue at the public inquiry, because this theory was not examined in detail. But given the evidence that the train from Balloch was stopped at the incoming signal, the reason for its doing so should have been ascertained at the inquiry.

In any case, the revised layout at Newton was potentially dangerous and should never have been allowed. Why did it take place? Did the civil engineer say: 'This is an unsatisfactory layout from an operating point of view, but it's the best that I can achieve within the space available in order to meet the wishes of the InterCity business'? Did the signal engineer say: 'I can signal this layout in accordance with the Standard Signalling Principles, but it's not a good layout from a train operating point of view'? Did the operating manager say: 'This is not a good layout from a train operating point of view, and I am not satisfied that it is acceptably safe either'? Perhaps they all made their views known but were ignored by the sponsor, InterCity.

Whilst it has to be accepted that the engineers could build and signal the layout in accordance with laid-down standards, the operating department was not bound to accept it. The operator could have said that in view of the recent experience of collisions on similar layouts he was not prepared

to sign off the scheme. No one could have compelled him to do so. Of course, he might have jeopardised his future career if he had stood his ground.

Why did the operator accept the scheme? It is probable that the reason can be found in British Rail's reorganisation on business lines a few years earlier, which resulted in the virtual emasculation of the Operating Department. The strong operating organisation that had existed almost from day one in railway history, running downwards from a chief operating superintendent at headquarters to district or divisional superintendents and on to stationmasters, had been abolished, and replaced by a much weaker organisation. It was a serious flaw in what was regarded by many people as a necessary change of emphasis in BR's organisation.

And what of the last line of defence: the nation's watchdog on matters of railway safety, HM Railway Inspectorate? It failed to learn the lesson of several previous accidents from a similar cause, details of which are given in the author's previous volume, *Hidden Dangers*. The formerly independent Railway Inspectorate, staffed by officers of great experience and judgement, had been taken over by the Health & Safety Executive (HSE), and was in the process of being watered down by the importation of people from other branches of the HSE with no railway experience at all, which might be regarded as an astonishing state of affairs.

Cowden

Cowden station lies on a branch line from Oxted to Uckfield. It had been double track throughout, but a decision was taken to single parts of the route as an economy measure. Long crossing loops were provided, including one at Ashurst, the station south of Cowden. It was 2 miles 903yd long. There were no facing trap points at the ends of the loops to prevent a train from wrongly passing on to a section of single line — there was no mandatory requirement for them. Reliance was placed on the driver's obedience to signals, supported by the Automatic Warning System (AWS). Mainly two-aspect colour-light signalling (red/green or yellow/green) was provided on a minimum basis.

Ashurst station is situated between a yellow/green (Distant) signal and the red/green (Stop) signal for which it acts as a repeater. The latter gives access to the single line and is therefore critical. It was equipped with AWS as an extra safeguard, but that was effective only if the AWS equipment on the train was operative. At that time, trains were allowed to run in certain circumstances with the trainborne AWS isolated (ie switched off) if the equipment had developed a fault, and there was certainly a suspicion that such circumstances had arisen in this case. The unit involved had a very bad fault record for AWS. Safety might therefore have depended entirely on the driver's correct observance of the signal at red. Could that be regarded as sufficiently safe on a misty morning? It could not, and therefore the Regulations demanded a maximum speed of 40mph in such weather conditions. The train actually travelled much faster.

The missing element in this case was a facing trap point where the double section of line became single. The question of the provision of trap points in such cases has been debated in the railway industry for many years, and there has been an increasing reluctance to provide them, partly based on cost, but also on the improvements which follow from the provision of colour-light signalling and AWS. If the sponsor of the scheme had demanded facing trap points at the ends of each loop (which would have required five in all) he would certainly have faced some resistance from both engineers and investment managers. It is an argument that still rages, but it should be an operating decision. It is not a proper decision for engineering departments.

Collision at Cowden, 15 October 1994.

The lack of facing trap points and the associated problem of whether to provide flank protection at junctions have been significant features in several of the fatal accidents in the 1990s, and the result of decisions made in the past. One of the main objections to facing trap points is the potential damage to a train if it should enter the trap points in the open position at a high speed and become derailed where the track ends shortly beyond them. In some cases there is a danger that the derailed train might foul an adjacent track. It is not a clear-cut issue, but in the Cowden case trap points could easily have been provided with a reasonable length of track and a sand drag beyond them, using part of the redundant double line. The fact that they were not provided is a reflection on the safety culture of the time, set against what was considered to be not just an acceptable standard of safety on the railway generally, but a very high standard of safety.

Maidenhead

This was one of a number of fuel tank fires on HSTs on the main West of England line from Paddington. A passenger was killed when he jumped out of the train after it had stopped, and was knocked down by a train on the next line. It neatly illustrates the fact that remaining in the interior of the train is generally, indeed almost always, preferable to making a rapid exit. There has been a great deal of woolly thinking on this question in recent years, and it will be discussed in more detail in later chapters.

Watford

The driver passed a signal at Danger at Watford South Junction and collided with a train that was crossing from one line to another in front of him. He had been properly warned about the red signal by the preceding signal showing one yellow, and the signal before that one showing two yellows (preliminary caution). There was an element of possible confusion and distraction by a number of permanent speed restrictions located quite close together between the two caution signals, one of which had been imposed because the overlap beyond the red signal was of sub-standard length (it was 162yd instead of the standard 200yd). The overlap is a safeguard in case the driver should misjudge his braking and pass a signal at Danger. If the overlap had been 200yd the accident would not have happened because the train actually stopped within that distance.

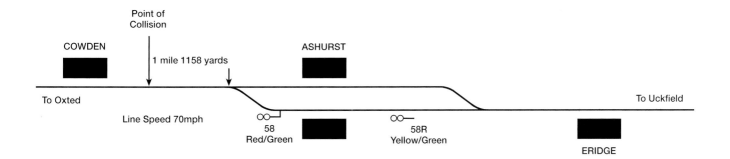

Significantly, the reduced overlap arose following re-modelling of the junction layout. The speed restriction that was introduced should have extended to the junction signal. Instead, it terminated some distance away, allowing a driver to accelerate and possibly overlook the fact that he had already passed a caution signal. The proper course would have been for the junction signals to be moved back to allow the 200yd overlap to be maintained, but that would have been costly. Imposing a speed restriction and putting the responsibility on the driver was a much cheaper, and far less satisfactory, option.

When the scheme was originally designed in BR days it was provided with standard overlaps of 200yd, but when the signal gantry was about to be erected it was discovered that it was too close to CEGB power lines passing overhead. The gantry was therefore positioned further towards Watford Junction, resulting in the overlap being reduced. It was then decided that delayed yellow aspect controls should be provided at signal No WJ755, and until this was done a temporary speed restriction should be applied on the approach to that signal, and continuing up to Signal WJ759.

However, privatisation and a change of organisation intruded. The delayed yellow aspect at Signal WJ755 was not introduced, and owing to complaints about trains being delayed over the temporary speed restriction its length was shortened and the restriction made permanent. The design of the scheme was corrupted in a way that would not have occurred in BR days. It was a product of privatisation. Needless to say, it was put right after the accident.

General conclusions from these accidents

A small sample of accidents can be misleading. Individual circumstances differ enormously. Small, almost irrelevant matters can play a major part in the number of casualties. However, there were two significant features:

1. The three most serious accidents — Newton, Cowden and Watford — were all caused by driver error, but all of them had an important underlying cause. In each case, the track and signalling had recently been remodelled, and in an unconventional manner so far as Newton and Cowden were concerned. The errors began on the drawing board, where too much was taken for granted. It was too readily assumed that drivers do not make mistakes, that AWS was infallible, and that modern signalling can safely signal any layout. There was a lack of railway professionalism and too much emphasis on cost. It was an object lesson that *safety begins on the drawing board*, otherwise there is a risk that the driver might be presented with an unsatisfactory, and hence potentially unsafe, layout.

2. The small number of casualties was mainly a matter of luck. Newton occurred late on a Sunday evening, where one train was just starting its journey, and the other was almost at the end. Both trains were very lightly loaded.

A Class 310 four-car electric multiple-unit is seen standing at Watford Junction station on 7 August 1986 with the 11.29 from Bletchley to Euston. *John E. Oxley*

Cowden happened at 8.28am on a Saturday morning when there were hardly any commuters about, just a few early shoppers. Watford happened in the shoulder of the peak and one of the trains involved was an empty stock train. The fates were extremely helpful. If the accidents had happened on ordinary weekdays, and in the rush hour, there might easily have been multiple casualties. But that's the way with accidents. Sometimes the fates are on your side; sometimes they are not.

Later in this book we shall find these two significant features still at work, but in a rather more perverse fashion. Old railwaymen used to judge the seriousness of an accident by its potential, and not its actual, consequences. The latter are in the hands of fate. We seem to have lost a measured, professional reaction to railway accidents in recent years.

How good was the standard of railway safety at privatisation?

Until the collision at Clapham in 1988, which killed 34 passengers and a driver, the standard of railway safety was generally regarded as being very high. Clapham was a watershed. It ought not to have been, because it was an isolated error in one spot, but somehow doubt was cast on the safety of the entire railway system. The media are not free from blame in that respect. A serious railway accident to busy commuter trains a couple of miles from the television studios is a godsend to the media. Unfortunately, it was followed by the Purley collision in March 1989 in which five passengers were killed, and the Glasgow Bellgrove collision two days later in which a driver and a passenger were killed.

Above and overleaf:
Clearance operations continued throughout the night following the collision near Clapham on 12 December 1988. *Jeremy de Souza*

The cause of the Clapham accident was unique so far as fatal train accidents are concerned — a wiring error by a signalling technician. Purley was caused by a driver ignoring AWS warnings and passing a red signal. Bellgrove was also caused by a driver passing a red signal, but in this case the signal was at the end of the platform at which the train had stopped for passenger purposes and was followed by a single lead junction — a danger that ought to have been foreseen on the drawing board.

How had the high standard of safety in the early 1990s been achieved?

The standard of safety in the period from 1990 up to privatisation was the highest in railway history. There were two main reasons for this:

1. British Rail had a very strong operating organisation which ran from top to bottom, from British Railways Board Headquarters to drivers and signalman and others at the workface, and similarly from bottom to top. It was a very effective chain of command. All accidents and incidents were investigated at source and reports were passed up the chain so that any changes to the Rules, systems, equipment or methods could be considered. Each level in the organisation was responsible for day-to-day safety in its own domain. It was a well-tried

organisation which in essence dated back to the 19th century, *and it worked*. Engineering departments had a similar structure and organisation, and there was inter-departmental co-operation at the various levels, not only informally but through standing committees too.

2. The lessons learned from accidents were cumulatively applied, resulting in a continuous improvement in the standard of safety achieved. Technical change often caused new problems, but also provided new opportunities for improved safety.

Perhaps there ought to be a third reason. Really serious accidents tend to occur at widely spaced intervals, and it was purely a matter of chance that there was none in this period.

What remained to be done at privatisation?

Recent experience had shown that the most serious potential cause of accidents was drivers passing signals at Danger, and that something effective needed to be done about it. AWS had been very valuable for many years but it was obsolete and not 100% effective. Something better was needed if higher standards of safety were to be achieved. This prompts the question of whether higher standards were needed. Only eight passenger deaths between 1990 and 1996 cannot be considered to provide adequate grounds for considerable expenditure on a replacement for AWS, but if circumstances had been different those eight could have been many more. The case for something better than AWS was very strong, and the British Railways Board had decided in November 1988 to adopt an automatic train protection system that would bring a train to a stand at a red signal irrespective of any failure on the driver's part. However, it proved technically very difficult to design a system that could be applied retrospectively to BR's many different types of traction, and the projected cost rose to such an extent that its justification began to be called into question. Eventually, in 1994, the scheme was abandoned, but it was still necessary to design something better than AWS. By now, Railtrack had been formed and it began rather slowly to design an enhanced AWS, which became the Train Protection & Warning System (TPWS). That was the position at the end of 1996.

❷ Privatisation — the safety implications

The nature of privatisation

Privatisation resulted in the fragmentation of the British Rail monolith on a massive scale. Not only that, but its whole nature and culture were changed. As part of the process, the infrastructure company was floated on the Stock Exchange, to be owned by a public limited company called Railtrack. Passenger train operations were planned to be split into 25 companies, known as Train Operating Companies (TOCs), based either on the line of an inter-city route or by area. The TOCs were considered to be transient organisations who bid for a franchise to operate passenger train services. They owned no assets and operated under franchise for a set number of years, on predetermined financial terms. The assets that the TOCs needed in order to operate trains, in respect of coaches and traction, were sold by BR at what

The major freight train operator following privatisation is the English, Welsh & Scottish Railway Ltd. One of its large and efficient fleet of Class 66 diesel-electric locomotives, No 66191, passes through Lostwithiel station on a china clay working in May 2000. *Author*

proved to be knockdown prices to three Train Leasing Companies who leased them back to the TOCs. New trains were funded by the Train Leasing Companies and leased to the particular TOC that ordered them. The TOCs paid Railtrack for the right to run trains and have access to the track.

Freight train operations were originally intended to be split into several freight companies dealing with different types of traffic, but ultimately the numbers were reduced. The shadow freight train companies established by BR just before privatisation were sold outright to new bidders, who owned them permanently. The sale included freight vehicles, locomotives and premises.

The maintenance and repair of locomotives and vehicles was dealt with in a number of ways. Some companies preferred to carry out light maintenance and repairs themselves, but heavier work was usually entrusted to a number of new companies established for that purpose and created from the former British Rail Engineering Ltd (BREL).

The maintenance and renewal of the infrastructure became a matter of some significance. Shadow companies were established by BR and were advertised for sale, being mainly bought by well-established civil engineering contractors.

Railtrack then issued maintenance and renewal contracts to a number of firms. Signal engineering and telecommunications were similarly dealt with, although some new firms were created.

Many other ancillary functions were sold off, and one of the most astonishing results was the almost overnight appearance of literally hundreds of small specialist firms and consultants to provide services and advice that BR had mainly done in-house.

To sum up, therefore:

1 Some companies were PLCs and owned assets (eg Railtrack).
2 Some companies were franchisees and owned no physical assets (ie TOCs).
3 Some companies owned trains, which they leased to TOCs (ie the Train Leasing Companies).
4 Some companies provided services under long-term contracts (ie civil engineering companies).
5 A host of companies, large and small, provided goods, services and advice on demand.

This was the outcome of the privatisation process. It created hundreds of separate units, large and small, permanent and transient. BR's carefully structured organisation, refined to operate efficiently, economically and safely, and by and large doing so with a fair measure of success, was completely demolished for ideological reasons. It was hoped, perhaps, that the result would be a reduction in the demands on the Treasury, and a system that was more responsive to the customer. It was lightly assumed by those who knew no better that there was a fair degree of 'fat' within BR which private enterprise would soon trim off.

The new companies quickly learned to their chagrin that BR had long ago trimmed off such fat as had ever existed.

Freightliner is another privatised freight operator, which initially specialised in container traffic. Class 57/0 diesel locomotive No 57010 *Freightliner Crusader* is seen near Mistley heading for Felixstowe on 25 July 2002. *Brian Morrison*

And what is even more astonishing, the Treasury and civil servants at the Department of Transport appear to have overlooked one of the elementary facts of life that all the hundreds of private companies now engaged in the operation and maintenance of the railway would do so only if there were profits to be made. A nationalised body such as BR had no shareholders demanding profits.

It is possible that the government believed that small, private companies were inherently more efficient, were more customer-oriented, were more enterprising and were quicker to react than a state-owned monolith. There is certainly a measure of truth in that, and it has been one of the successes of the privatised railway. There was also the question of easier access to private capital and the ability of being able to plan long-term, but the nature of privatisation and the government's insatiable desire to interfere and meddle has made those two very desirable developments less certain. If the railway industry is to prosper, its organisation needs to change and the government needs to stop meddling. Unfortunately, no modern government can resist the temptation. Witness the demise of Railtrack and the creation in its stead of a new not-for-profit company, a company limited by guarantee, called Network Rail. It has no shareholders and is virtually owned by the government. At one time it would have been called nationalisation, but to satisfy the needs of Treasury accounting it is not regarded as such. That is certainly an advantage.

What was the potential effect upon safety?

This enormous *mélange* of organisations has to work efficiently and co-operatively if safety is not to be imperilled. The Department of Transport realised that safety was at risk unless a new organisation was created to replace that which had existed under BR. The Health & Safety Executive (HSE) was asked to consider and report on this problem and it recommended the 'safety case' system used in some industries

elsewhere. Under this system, every company has to have an approved safety case, setting out how it will conduct its operations with risks reduced to a level as low as reasonably practicable. In the case of the railway industry, Railtrack was given the responsibility of examining and approving the safety cases of all the passenger and freight train operators.

This, of course, assumed that Railtrack would have the necessary operating, safety and technical expertise properly to undertake such a duty, which was by no means certain. It ought to have been the duty of HM Railway Inspectorate (HMRI) but there were problems in that direction. HMRI was a small organisation and could not have taken on the duty of validating and monitoring safety cases without an increase in staff, the prospect of which did not suit the Treasury. Obtaining such staff with the necessary qualifications and experience would not have been easy, on top of which the HSE would have had to pay the market rate for such personnel. In fact, obtaining such qualified staff has always been a problem for the HSE because it has not been allowed to pay the going rate, so it has taken the easy and foolish way out by transferring staff, with no experience of the railway industry, from other HSE sections. As we shall see in a later chapter, Lord Cullen, who held a public inquiry into the Ladbroke Grove accident, rightly considered this to be unsatisfactory.

The safety case became the approved method of achieving safety on the 'new' railway. Railtrack's own safety case was validated by HMRI, which thus established Railtrack as the virtual custodian of safety, a responsibility that it was not really equipped to fulfil.

Freightliner has now expanded into heavy haul. A new Class 66/5 diesel-electric locomotive, No 66538, arrives at Dagenham with a rake of new heavy-haul Autoflat wagons on 15 January 2002. *Brian Morrison*

The safety of train operation then depended on a number of things:

1. The robustness and scope of the train operators' safety cases, in ensuring that their staffs were properly trained, adequate in number and performed their duties in a safe manner.
2. The maintenance of rolling stock in a properly serviceable condition, whether performed by train operators themselves, or by specialist firms under contract.
3. The maintenance of the infrastructure to a satisfactory standard. This work was the responsibility of a number of engineering firms under contract with Railtrack.
4. A safe system of operation and signalling, as set out in the Rules, Regulations and other instructions. These were inherited from British Rail and initially needed little change. Railtrack created a Safety & Standards Directorate to be responsible for these matters, among others.
5. It was necessary for Railtrack to monitor the standard of safety being achieved, to investigate accidents, to learn lessons and to introduce whatever changes were desirable. Railtrack was the lead organisation in this respect.

What were the hidden dangers?

The privatisation process resulted in the signalling of trains becoming the responsibility of Railtrack, even though it was an operating function and Railtrack was basically responsible for the infrastructure. Indeed, it initially considered itself a property owning company, a situation that stored up trouble for the future. Responsibility for the signalling of trains was given to Railtrack because it was a system-wide company and it was thought that it would deal dispassionately and fairly with demands from train operators for train paths and priorities, whereas if the train operators had been responsible for train signalling in their own areas there might have been disputes from other train operators running through those areas.

The freight operators were particularly concerned about this. The timetabling and priority in day-to-day operation of freight trains had changed over the years and it was no longer reasonable to give total priority to passenger trains. Many freight trains ran at almost express passenger train speeds and the traffic they carried was often very time sensitive. Freight customers demanded a high standard of service and punctuality, and if it was not provided there was the constant fear that they would quickly take their business elsewhere. This is important, as freight operators have to pay their way, which many of the passenger train operators, occupying track slots with their frequent but minimal length trains, do not.

Signallers had traditionally given priority to trains depending on their classification. Passenger trains were in Classes 1 and 2, whilst freight trains were in lower classes. It was a rough and ready system, which had been satisfactory in bygone years but was no longer appropriate. In BR days the Control organisation had intervened when necessary to adjust priorities, but on the privatised railway, with delays to trains incurring financial penalties for Railtrack, a different system was required and a protocol was agreed between the various train operators which gave an improved priority to freight trains. Such a protocol could just as easily have been achieved if train signalling had been the responsibility of the predominant train operator on a particular route. If the number of TOCs on a route is reduced, as suggested by the Strategic Rail Authority, it would be even more logical for train signalling to be dealt with in this manner.

The unforeseen consequences, the hidden danger, of the signalling of trains belonging to one organisation, Railtrack, and the operation of trains by drivers belonging to another, the Train Operating Companies, all 30 or so of them, were to prove fatal — literally. In BR days, the operation of trains, including the signalling, had belonged entirely to one department — the Operating Department. There were no hidden interfaces: it was one cohesive operation. Under privatisation, there were the train operators on the one hand and Railtrack on the other. It was anomalous that Railtrack, essentially responsible for the infrastructure, should have any concerns for the day-to-day operation of trains. It led to the establishment of two Control organisations, running in parallel but often physically separate. Signallers reported to the Railtrack control office; drivers reported to the TOC control office. It was a dangerous split, and considerably increased the likelihood of vital messages going astray or of being misunderstood. It was almost certainly a factor in the Southall collision.

As noted above, Railtrack, through its Safety & Standards Directorate (S&SD), was responsible for the Rule Book and other operating instructions, but much of the vital intelligence that the S&SD required to consider whether any changes needed to be made resided in the train operators' organisations. Drivers were a particularly effective source for recognising changes that needed to be made and for the early detection of unsatisfactory situations. This especially applied to signalling, for drivers were at the receiving end and it was vital that the message that the signaller gave through his signals was received and correctly acted upon by the driver. But drivers belonged to many different organisations, widely separated from Railtrack and its S&SD, both physically and conceptually. In the early years, relations between TOCs and Railtrack were often negative. It was a commercial relationship, whereas it should have been an operational one. Railtrack often had a superior attitude in its dealings with the TOCs. It regarded itself as the railway, and the TOCs as transient people. These factors were to be predominant in the Ladbroke Grove collision.

The care of the infrastructure

In principle, there would seem to be nothing wrong in the concept of the maintenance of the infrastructure being carried out by private companies under contract, but it presupposes that the terms of the contract are such as to lead to a high standard of maintenance. It also presupposes that the contractors actually deliver the contract. Was it sufficient for Railtrack to assume that the contractors would do this, without any form of supervision or check? If the contractors had been carrying out maintenance under contract for several years at a high standard there might have been some relaxation on the need for a check on the quality of delivery, but it was a new field. Relationships between Railtrack and the contractors were new and untested. In such circumstances it was clear that Railtrack should have had its own engineering inspectors to check on the manner in which the contract was delivered, or at the very least have employed a reliable third party, such as engineering consultants, to do so. It was not done. Front-line staff wondered how Railtrack could become such a celebrated cash-rich highflyer when the track continued visibly to deteriorate.

In BR days, indeed through the whole lifetime of railways pre-privatisation, there was a strong Civil Engineering Department which encompassed all aspects of the maintenance and renewal of the infrastructure — ie track, earthworks, bridges and other structures — and everything necessary for trains to run on safely. Permanent-way inspectors knew every inch of their tracks and reported to Area or Divisional Civil Engineers, who in turn reported to Chief Civil Engineers of the railways or regions. That chain of command, staffed with highly experienced and qualified civil engineers, was its strength. It was destroyed at privatisation and nothing remotely similar took its place. Thus were the seeds of the Hatfield and Potters Bar disasters sown.

A splendid shot of a Class 158/0 diesel multiple-unit on the heavily congested section between Manchester Oxford Road and Manchester Piccadilly on 27 July 2001. The train is the First North Western 10.43 from Llandudno. *Brian Morrison*

This might have been considered the weakest link in the whole privatisation process. The danger was clearly foreseen during the progress of the Railways Bill, and several experienced railwaymen pointed it out, but they were ignored. The government was anxious to complete the privatisation before the next general election, which it was likely to lose, and could not afford the delay that a careful study of expert comment might cause.

One solution to the problem would be for Railtrack to take responsibility for the maintenance of the infrastructure 'in house' and cease relying upon contractors. Railtrack could then replicate BR's Civil Engineering Department, but continue to rely upon contractors for track renewals. It would then have a clear knowledge of the state of its assets, and that knowledge would enable it to impose speed restrictions when the state of the track pointed to the need for such action. However, it would be a major organisational change. Railtrack would have to create a completely new department and each Railtrack zone would have to take on all the additional staff necessary, who are presently employed by contractors. Some of them might not wish to transfer, especially the more experienced and qualified engineers.

It would also be another upheaval, but the end product would be very desirable. However, the early enthusiasm for such a change has evaporated and it is now seen to be more desirable to ensure that contractors are properly instructed, controlled and monitored. That is what was missing at Hatfield. Getting the track right is a fundamental requirement, and in many ways more important than the installation of the European Train Control System. Whilst the latter is a European Union directive, the Strategic Rail Authority can give a derogation on economic grounds exempting fitment. But that is the world of politics which has bedevilled railways throughout their history.

There are those who cry for the renationalisation of Railtrack, in the simplistic belief that everything would be all right if there were no need to make a profit for the shareholders. At first sight it might be an attractive proposition, but those who make it obviously have no knowledge or experience of the trials and tribulations of the nationalised railway under political masters who could not resist meddling and interfering, and a Treasury which turned the investment tap on and off, depending on the state of the national economy. Of course, not all political interference is bad, and it is the quality of the interference that counts. Railway chiefs may not always appreciate this and know how to influence politicians positively.

Current safety regulation

The HSE, through HMRI, is currently responsible for the safety regulation of the railway industry, and Lord Cullen has recommended that it be given enough properly qualified staff,

The Virgin Rail Group Co acquired the franchise to run passenger trains on the West Coast main line. One of its trains in its distinctive livery is seen entering Euston station in 2002, behind electric locomotive No 87016. These rather elderly, but still comfortable, trains will soon be replaced by the 'Pendolinos'. *D. C. Hall*

The franchise for operating the suburban services from Euston was acquired by Silverlink Train Services Ltd. One of its Class 313 electric multiple-units in its very colourful livery is seen entering Euston station in 2002. These units were originally built for inner suburban services from King's Cross in 1976/7. It is now a requirement that external doors on trains be painted in a different colour from the remainder of the train. The Strategic Rail Authority is considering merging the franchises operated by Silverlink and Virgin Rail into one franchise. *D. C. Hall*

and a sufficiently powerful boss, to enable it to do so effectively. But it must concentrate on becoming more professional and less bureaucratic. That will give it greater self-confidence, which in turn should lead to a less confrontational and more understanding approach. For the best results HMRI and the industry need to work together. HMRI must remember that railwaymen, too, are interested in safety, and having a safety regulator in no way removes any safety responsibilities from the industry itself. Each company must carry out its responsibilities safely, so that there is overall safety.

Lord Cullen recommended that the investigation of accidents should cease to be the responsibility of the HSE, but should be transferred to a new Railway Accidents Investigation Branch (RAIB). It will be interesting to see how HSE will react to the loss of this high-profile part of its empire, and how Cullen's recommendation will be fleshed out. He has nominated the Health & Safety Commission (HSC) to take action to establish the RAIB and the devil will be in the detail. A Parliamentary Bill was published on 14 January 2003, and the contents are discussed in Chapter 14.

There is another player who should be mentioned in this chapter — the Rail Regulator. The office was a new creation of the Railway Act 1993 and was obviously thought to be of considerable importance, judged by the fact that the Act commences in Sec 1 (1): 'The Secretary of State shall appoint an officer to be known as the Rail Regulator', and continues by setting out a lengthy list of his functions. The Regulator is required in Sec 4 (3)(a): 'to take into account the need to protect all persons from dangers arising from the operation of the railways', which is a reminder to the Regulator to take care that his regulatory actions, such as an insistence upon improvements in punctuality, do not have an adverse effect upon safety.

❸ Nemesis: the Southall accident — 19 September 1997

SINCE 1990, Britain's railways had enjoyed a standard of safety unparalleled in their long history. Only eight passengers had lost their lives in train accidents in almost eight years, and to put it into perspective that is fewer than are lost on Britain's roads in a single day. It was unrealistic to think that such a golden era could last for ever, and it came to an end at 1.14pm on Friday, 19 September 1997 at Southall, on the West of England main line into Paddington.

This was on the old Great Western Railway main line, which had a safety record second to none, thanks largely to the policy adopted by the GWR of installing an automatic train control system in the 1930s. Indeed, the section of line between Reading and Paddington, on which this accident took place, had been equipped before World War 1. GWR

A graphic picture of the crash at Southall on 19 September 1997 when the 10.32 Great Western Trains HST from Swansea to Paddington ran past a signal at danger and collided with a train of empty aggregate wagons which was crossing its path. *Rail magazine/Philip Haigh*

men were proud of their safety record and proud of their company. Rightly so. What could have gone so wrong?

The scene shifts now to Cardiff. Train No 1A47, the 10.32 HST from Swansea to Paddington ran into Cardiff Central station, where there was a crew change. Driver Tunnock brought the train in and was relieved by Driver Harrison. A perfectly normal and routine crew change. Tunnock informed Harrison that the Automatic Warning System (AWS) had been switched off because it was faulty, but Harrison was not apparently concerned and felt himself quite capable of driving to Paddington at 125mph, alone in the driving cab, without the reassurance of the AWS, and without ever having driven an HST without the AWS in operation.

Driver Harrison's train was also equipped with the BR Automatic Train Protection (BR-ATP) system and it was in working order. However, it was not in use because neither Tunnock nor Harrison was currently qualified to drive a train with the ATP in use. ATP is a superior system to AWS and would have fully safeguarded the train had it been in use. The reasons for this state of affairs will be explained later.

The scene of the crash at Southall on 19 September 1997, looking towards Paddington. The 10.32 HST from Swansea to Paddington crashed into a train of empty bogie hopper wagons, which was slowly threading its way across the path of the HST into some sidings. *Ken Brunt*

After all, it was a fine, clear day and the driving cab was equipped with both a Driver's Safety Device (DSD), known colloquially as the Deadman's Pedal, and a Driver's Vigilance Device (DVD) which emitted a warbling tone every minute. The DVD had to be acknowledged by the driver releasing the DSD pedal and immediately reapplying pressure with his foot. If he failed to do so the brakes would come on. This was bound to keep the driver alert or, at the worst, quickly bring him back to a state of alertness if he had become less than alert in the previous 60 seconds.

In any event, Driver Harrison took charge of the train and set off for Paddington, booked departure time 11.25. The train called intermediately at Newport, Bristol Parkway and Swindon, and left Reading, the final stop, just before 1.00pm for the final leg of the journey to Paddington. HSTs are allowed 33 minutes on this service for the 36 miles to Paddington, but that includes several minutes' 'recovery time' to allow for any minor delays *en route* and still reach Paddington on time. It helps to improve the punctuality statistics, but it is a device which dates back many years, and certainly pre-dates privatisation. Southall is only nine miles from Paddington.

The line between Reading and Paddington is very busy and trains are often checked by adverse signals, although HST drivers would expect to be given a clear road whenever possible. However, it is implicit that such an expectation must not lead to any complacency on the driver's part; he must still observe signals in the normal manner. But the scene now shifts to the signalling centre that controls the movement of trains in the Southall area. It is known as Slough New signalbox, and is officially an Integrated Electronic Control Centre (IECC). The main duty of the signallers is to control the running of trains in such a manner that delays are kept to the minimum — in practice they are regulators rather than signallers.

A freight train, No 6V17, was approaching Southall from the London direction and was destined for Brentford Sidings at Southall, which required it to cross the path of Driver Harrison's approaching HST. The signaller decided that, bearing in mind other trains approaching Southall on other lines, his optimum course of action was to run the freight train into the sidings first, then clear the signals for the HST. The automatic route setting system allowed him to do so because the approaching HST had not quite arrived at the point at which the route through Southall would be locked for it. The freight train slowly made its way across the line on which the HST was approaching at 125mph.

The signaller was fully entitled to make such a decision. It was entirely in accordance with the Rules. All regulating decisions are made on the basis that drivers will obey signals, and that is how the railways have always been worked. It would create a quite impossible situation if signallers had to consider whether, before signalling a conflicting move, a driver might fail to stop at a signal at Danger. It would also place a quite unfair burden on the signaller. Whether the signaller would have acted differently if he had been informed that the HST was running without the AWS being operative is open to doubt, and the Signalling Regulations would certainly not have required him to do so.

However, before taking our story further, it is necessary to describe the track, the signalling and the trains.

The track

There are four running lines (tracks) at Southall. They run east and west, and the names of the lines are, reading from north to south, the up relief line ('up' signifies the London direction), the down relief line, the up main line and the down main line. The maximum permitted speed on the main lines is 125mph.

At Southall there are crossovers that allow trains to be switched from one line to another, and these allow, among other moves, a train to be crossed from the down relief line (on which the freight train was approaching) to the sidings situated on the south side of the running lines.

The signalling

All the signals for the running lines are of the standard four-aspect colour-light type, capable of displaying one red light or one yellow light or two yellow lights or one green light. A red light means 'Danger — Stop at this signal'. However, a train travelling at 125mph requires well over a mile and a quarter in which to stop and it is essential to give the driver a prior indication that he is approaching a red signal. Signals are situated about three-quarters of a mile apart; therefore when a signal is showing red (called a red aspect), the next signal in rear, three-quarters of a mile back, will show a yellow aspect, and the signal in rear of that will show two yellow lights (called a double yellow aspect). The Rule Book instructions give the following definitions:

Red light	*Danger*	*Stop*
One yellow light	Caution	Proceed; be prepared to stop at the next signal
Two yellow lights (vertically displayed)	Preliminary Caution	Proceed; be prepared to find the next signal displaying one yellow light

Other types of signal are used to control the movement of trains having to proceed from a running line to a siding.

The running lines at Southall are equipped with track circuits throughout their length. Individual track circuits are of varying lengths, depending on the track layout, and each track circuit is electrically insulated from its neighbour. A weak electric current is passed along the track circuit, keeping an electrical relay activated, but when the wheels of a train pass over that section of line the electric current is diverted through them, the relay is deactivated and the track circuit is said to be 'occupied'. An occupied track circuit controls or initiates several functions. It may place a signal to Danger, or maintain it at Danger. It may lock points. It denotes to a signaller the presence of a train. It is an integral part of train running information systems.

The trains

The High Speed Train (HST) was train No 1A47, the 10.32 from Swansea to London Paddington. It was single-manned, ie there was only the one driver in the driving cab. It was operated by Great Western Trains (GWT) and was marshalled in the following order:

Power car No 43173
Two first class coaches (H and G)
Buffet car (F)
Four standard class coaches (E, C, B and A)
Power car No 43163.

HSTs had been operating between Paddington and Swansea for about 20 years.

The freight train was train No 6V17, the 09.58 from Allington to Southall. It was hauled by a Mendip Rail Class 59 diesel-electric locomotive, No 59101, and consisted of 20 empty bogie hopper wagons used for carrying aggregate.

The British Railways Automatic Warning System (BR-AWS)

Immediately after nationalisation in 1948 the then Railway Executive decided to embark upon a project to design and install an automatic warning system as a protection against drivers inadvertently passing Danger signals. However, main lines of the former Great Western Railway were already equipped with that company's Automatic Train Control (ATC) system, which had been developed before World War 1 and had been installed on all its main lines in the 1930s. The GWR system worked in the following manner. Equipment in the form of a long ramp was located longitudinally between the rails at Distant signals. Along the top of the ramp ran a metal strip which engaged with a spring-loaded 'shoe' located underneath a locomotive. When the Distant signal was in the 'clear' position the ramp was electrified and an electric current passed through the shoe and rang a bell in the engine cab. When the Distant signal was at 'Caution', the electric current was switched off. The raising of the shoe then broke

The beginnings of the BR Automatic Warning System. The 'receiver' fitted under the front of Class A4 steam locomotive No 60007 is seen passing over the magnet fixed in the track. The photograph is undated but is likely to have been taken in the early 1950s. *BR*

an electric circuit on the engine and caused a steam whistle to blow. The driver had to operate equipment to acknowledge the sounding of the steam whistle, and if he failed to do so the brakes would be applied automatically. It was an excellent system, designed for the Absolute Block System of Signalling and lineside signalboxes, and gave the Great Western Railway a very good safety record.

Following nationalisation in 1948, the newly formed Railway Executive considered that a system that required physical contact between a ramp and a shoe was not suitable for future development, and it developed a non-contact system (AWS), using the same principles. The ramp was replaced by a permanent magnet and an electro-magnet, and the shoe was replaced by a receiver. When a signal is at 'Clear', the electro-magnet is energised and causes a bell in the driving cab to give a short ring. When a signal is at anything other than 'Clear', the electro-magnet is inoperative, and the permanent magnet causes a warning horn to sound in the driving cab. If the driver does not acknowledge it within a few seconds, the brakes will be applied automatically. The former GWR ATC equipment was eventually replaced by the BR-AWS equipment. Modern Track Circuit Block Signalling, with its steady succession of signals, all fitted with AWS, requires a driver to acknowledge the warning quite frequently, and has the potential to cause the system to lose some of its effectiveness through such repetition.

The BR Automatic Train Protection System

BR-AWS might have been considered to be more or less foolproof. If the driver failed to acknowledge a warning, the brakes would be applied automatically. If he acknowledged a warning he could hardly forget a few seconds later that he had to apply the brakes. But the weakness of the system was the absence of any check to see that the driver had actually responded to the warning, and cases continued to appear in which drivers had actually failed to apply the brakes after acknowledging a warning, resulting in a collision. It was a situation that could not be allowed to continue.

Accordingly, the British Railways Board (BRB) decided in November 1988 to adopt a system of automatic train protection which did check that the driver was responding to a signal requiring him to brake. The system chosen checked continuously, from the first warning, that the speed of the train was being reduced to an extent that would enable it to stop at the Danger signal ahead. An on-board computer calculated the braking curve, ie the rate of retardation, that would enable the train to stop at the Danger signal, and compared it continuously with the actual speed of the train. If the speed was too high, the brakes would be applied without any action by the driver.

A specification was produced and in 1990 a contract was awarded to ACEC Transport, a signalling contractor, to equip the line between Paddington and Bristol with a form of automatic train protection, as a proving site for system evaluation and equipment testing. A similar trial was also arranged for the Chiltern line from Marylebone, using a different contractor. The BRB had decided, quite rightly, that it was necessary to evaluate ATP systems thoroughly before embarking on widespread installation.

The BR Automatic Train Protection speedometer fitted in the cab of a Great Western Trains HST. *Author*

However, the development process ran into serious technical difficulties with the retrofitting of ATP equipment to the HSTs used on the trains between Paddington and Bristol, and it was very difficult to obtain reliable operation in daily service. Furthermore, the estimated costs were rising rapidly, and questions began to be asked about the cost-effectiveness of a national application of the system. In 1995, the Health & Safety Commission, having taken advice from HM Railway Inspectorate (HMRI), recommended to the Secretary of State for Transport that a case could not be made for proceeding with ATP on cost-effective grounds and that an alternative system should be developed. This alternative became the Train Protection & Warning System (TPWS), which is calculated to provide 70% of the benefits of ATP at a fraction of the cost, and be available much more quickly. At the same time, the Driver's Reminder Appliance was introduced. The driver operates this when his train is standing in a station platform with the signal ahead at Danger, and in other circumstances.

With the abandonment of the ATP trials, there was no longer any need to continue using the equipment on the Paddington line, but it would have been wasteful to have abandoned it and lose the additional protection that it gave. It therefore remained in use, but there were difficulties and expense in maintaining it in a serviceable condition. It was not regarded as a high priority, hence many trains ran with the equipment out of use. Drivers still had the assurance of AWS.

The control organisations

In BR days, there were Control Offices at all main centres, covering the surrounding areas, so that the operation of trains and the movement of traffic on virtually the entire railway network fell within the monitoring and jurisdiction of a Control Office.

Most trains run according to a prearranged plan, set out in the working timetables. The appropriate locomotives, coaches and multiple-unit sets are programmed, together with the necessary traincrews. However, train running does not always follow the plan. It deviates for many reasons and it is then the function of the Control organisation to intervene and to restore the working to normal as quickly as possible. Deviations can be caused by blockages of the line from mishaps, failures of train, track or signalling, untoward events such as suicides on the line, lorries hitting bridges where the railway crosses over the road, floods; the list is legion. In addition, it is sometimes necessary to run special trains at short notice, particularly in the freight business, and it is then the duty of the Control organisation to arrange for such trains to run, and to provide relief traincrews during the journey. Put simply, it is the duty of the Control organisation to restore the working to normal as quickly as possible after a deviation and to make the most economical use of assets and staff.

In BR days, all the staff concerned in the operation and running of trains responded to the same Control organisation. However, resulting from privatisation there was a split between traincrews and signallers. Traincrews belong to Train Operating Companies (TOCs), whilst signallers belong to Railtrack. Each company has its own Control organisation. Great Western Trains (GWT) had its Control Office at Swindon. Railtrack had its Operations Control in the same room. This proximity should have enabled the accurate and timely passage of important messages, but the division of Control responsibility became a significant factor in the accident, as we shall see.

The course of events leading up to the accident

The story starts on the evening before the day of the accident, and it is necessary to trace the movements of the HST concerned. On Thursday 18 September 1997 that HST worked the 18.02 from Paddington to Oxford. Everything was in order except the driver/guard communication system. After the train had arrived at Oxford it was shunted across to the up main line for its return journey to Paddington, but as it ran slowly into the up platform the AWS warning horn sounded as the front of the train passed over the AWS ramp for the signal ahead. The driver acknowledged the warning in the usual manner by pressing the AWS button, thus preventing the brakes from being applied automatically, but the warning horn continued to sound as though the acknowledgement button had not been pressed. Consequently, the brakes were applied automatically, bringing the train to a stand halfway down the platform. In order to silence the warning horn and release the brakes, and enable the train to be drawn fully into the platform, the driver had to isolate the AWS equipment.

Isolation of the AWS equipment on the train is necessary from time to time and is covered by instructions to staff in the Rule Book Appendix No 8. These state that:

'The driver must isolate the AWS if cancellation of a warning indication does not stop the horn or brake application.' (The driver did this.)

'The driver must inform the signalman at the first convenient opportunity.' (He told the station supervisor what had happened and asked him to obtain permission from the signalman to draw the train forward to the signal. The driver did not speak directly to the signalman to inform him of the AWS isolation. This was an omission that was to prove significant, because it resulted in Railtrack Operations Control being unaware of the AWS isolation. The signalman recalled being informed that the brakes had gone on and that the driver had reset the brake. He did not recall any mention of the AWS being isolated.)

'If the signalman is advised that the AWS has been isolated he must inform Railtrack Operations Control.' (The signalman did not do this because he did not recall any mention of the AWS being isolated.)

'The train must be taken out of service at the first suitable location, without causing delay or cancellation.' (This could not be done at Oxford.)

'The driver must record the details in the Repair Book.' (He did this. A Repair Book is carried in the driving cab on all traction units, and is for the information of maintenance and servicing staff.)

The HST was then driven to Paddington without further incident, but with the AWS out of use. The driver was allowed to do this under the regulations applicable at the time. After the passengers had alighted, the train was taken to Old Oak Common Maintenance Depot for overnight servicing. At this stage, the driver should have completed an Incident Report form but did not do so. It would have drawn the attention of the depot staff to the AWS fault. However, the depot staff became aware of the fault when they read the driver's entry in the Repair Book. They carried out a test, which revealed no fault (in fact, the AWS reset switch had contamination on its electrical contact surfaces which rendered its performance intermittent and the fault would have been difficult to trace without detailed examination) and they therefore reset the AWS isolation switch, bringing the AWS back into operation. Intermittent faults in equipment are frequently difficult to find, may need special equipment and may entail a lengthy process.

According to the report of the inquiry, Driver Tunnock took charge of the HST at Old Oak Common early on the morning of Friday 19 September 1997 and drove it to Paddington, using the cab in which the AWS had been isolated the previous evening. As he left the depot the train passed over an AWS test magnet, which sounded the horn. He was able to cancel the horn by pressing the acknowledgement button in the normal way. On arrival at Paddington, he shut down the engine and walked to the other end of the train, where he found that the driver/guard communication system was not working. Returning to the power car at the buffer stops he inserted his master key to activate the system, so that he could restart the engine. The AWS horn sounded at once,

A Thames Trains Class 166 diesel unit approaches Hayes & Harlington station on the down main line on 1 October 2002 and passes under the signal gantry carrying signal No SN280 for the up main line. This signal is displaying two yellow aspects (a double yellow). It is the signal which Driver Harrison failed to respond to, and was displaying a double yellow on that day. *Author*

and he was unable to silence it. He therefore had to operate the AWS isolation switch to release the brakes. It had no effect on the journey from Paddington to Swansea, but was to be a critical factor on the return journey.

Driver Tunnock then went to the Operations Supervisor's office and reported both problems to Mr Barnfield. The latter attempted to contact the station fitter, but without success. Mr Barnfield next contacted GWT Control at Swindon by phone and handed the telephone to Driver Tunnock, who explained the situation and asked for fitters to attend to the train at Swansea. Driver Tunnock should have reported the matter to the signalman, but no doubt thought it better to speak directly to GWT Control. However, no one in GWT Control subsequently admitted receiving Driver Tunnock's message, so nothing was done. Railtrack Control was therefore still unaware of any AWS defect, or any isolation of the equipment.

When the HST arrived at Swansea, Driver Tunnock was surprised to find no fitters in attendance. He telephoned GWT Control, but again no one in GWT Control could be found subsequently who admitted receiving Driver Tunnock's message. That might be considered strange. He then spoke to the Station Services Manager at Swansea, who telephoned the GWT depot at Landore, 10 minutes away, to request assistance. Then, almost incredibly, there followed yet more confusion. The fitters attended to the driver/guard communication system, but not the AWS. It has to be said that the extent of confusion about messages does GWT no credit, and there were several opportunities to attend to the AWS, but all might have been in vain because the failure was

intermittent. The HST was therefore allowed to depart from Swansea for Paddington without the safety assurance of AWS, and without any other precautions being taken. The Rule Book allowed this, which might seem odd. The Automatic Train Protection System could have saved the day. It was in working order, but. as mentioned earlier, neither of the drivers on the Swansea–Paddington journey was currently qualified to use it, and therefore it was switched off. Also, as mentioned earlier, it was not a requirement that it should be in use, but it would have been a useful alternative in the event of AWS failure.

After leaving Reading on the up main line, the HST encountered a number of emergency speed restrictions of 100mph which had been imposed owing to the condition of the track. This was a routine procedure that applied throughout the railway system whenever circumstances required it. Driver Harrison observed the restrictions, then accelerated to the maximum permitted line speed of 125mph. Approaching Southall there are the following four-aspect colour-light signals, with the aspects which they were exhibiting to Driver Harrison:

Signal SN298, showing green
Signal SN280, showing two yellows, 1,109yd (1,018m)
    from SN298
Signal SN270, showing one yellow, 1,158yd (1,056m)
    from SN280
Signal SN254, showing red, 1,672yd (1,530m)
    from SN270.

From SN254 to the fouling point of the crossovers ahead was 448yd (410m).

Driver Harrison should have prepared to apply the brake when signal SN280 came into view, exhibiting two yellows, but he failed to react. He similarly failed to react when the next signal, SN270, came into view exhibiting one yellow. Under normal circumstances he would by now have acknowledged two AWS warnings and have applied the brake. The situation was becoming very desperate indeed. From SN270 to the point of collision with the freight train which was crossing his path was just under a mile, not quite enough to enable the train to be stopped clear, which would have required at least 1¼ miles. Unfortunately, about half of the reduction in speed from 125mph occurs in the last quarter of a mile.

Driver Harrison finally reacted when he saw signal SN254 in the distance exhibiting a red aspect at about the same time as he passed the signal displaying one yellow, and he probably saw at the same moment the wagons of the freight train crossing his path. His feelings at that moment are perhaps beyond imagining. He was hurtling towards a massive obstruction at over two miles a minute, which is about 60yd a second, with absolutely no possibility of avoiding a thunderous collision in which he stood a fair chance of being killed instantly. In that respect, he joined a long line of drivers who, over the centuries, had found themselves in a similar predicament, although never before at 125mph.

It is difficult to find any case in recorded history where a driver has reacted to an imminent Danger signal when travelling at more than 75mph. That is mainly due to the widespread extension of AWS in recent decades on high-speed main lines on which speeds have increased concurrently. After Driver Harrison had applied the brake he made his escape from the driving cab and went back through the bulkhead door into the narrow gangway to the left of the engine. He was fortunate that the impact and damage to the power car occurred on the other side and that the power car remained upright as it cannoned off the wagons of the freight train. He was uninjured apart from cuts and bruises, but quite understandably he was severely shocked.

Did passengers on the train have any premonition or inkling of imminent disaster? It is highly unlikely. In the 1990s the railways had passed through the safest period in their history, and all the accidents which had occurred had involved multiple-unit trains on suburban duties. It was rare for a main line express to be involved. Perhaps they looked up from their newspapers when they felt the brakes go on sharply, but more in concern that the train might be delayed, rather than fears that they were going to experience the effects of a collision at considerable speed. In fact, the express was travelling at over 60mph at the point of impact.

Damage to the HST, and casualties

The leading power car made scraping contact with the wagons of the freight train and suffered severe damage to its bodyside. It was diverted to the left and derailed, but remained upright.

Coach H fell on to its left-hand side and came to rest after colliding with one of the structures supporting the overhead electric line. It carried 12 passengers, two of whom were killed.

Coach G suffered severe damage to its side after contact with a wagon. It became wedged under the wagon and was forced into considerable distortion by the weight and momentum of the remainder of the train. There were 14 passengers in this coach. Four of them were killed and one died later in hospital. The remainder were all injured, more or less seriously.

Coaches F, E and C were derailed but remained generally upright.

The remainder of the train was not derailed.

The rate of deceleration from over 60mph was very severe indeed, occurring in a few seconds over a very short distance. Driver Harrison survived, but seven passengers lost their lives. Many passengers suffered some injury, several of them seriously.

A formal public inquiry was held, and its salient features form the basis of the next chapter.

Note — although some of the features of this accident were explained in the previous volume *Hidden Dangers*, published in 1999, many significant factors had not been revealed at the time.

A train of bogie hopper wagons, similar to those involved in the collision at Southall, passes slowly through the rebuilt Leeds station in October 2002. *Author*

④ Southall — what went wrong?

WHAT went wrong is very easy to answer. The driver went past a signal at Danger because he didn't react to the preceding cautionary signals. It is as simple as that. All the rest — the alignment of the signals, the signalman routeing a freight train across the path of the express, the questionable standard of maintenance of the AWS equipment, the errors in passing verbal and telephone messages — might be considered to be red herrings. They are not totally irrelevant, but typical of some of the accompaniments to most accidents.

There is nothing new in drivers passing signals at Danger, although a disinterested observer might conclude that it was a new phenomenon from the furore which followed the Southall accident. The fact is that drivers have been passing signals at Danger ever since lineside signals came into use in the mid-19th century and it did not take long before inventive minds were designing and developing technical means of preventing such occurrences. Indeed, as early as 1858 one of the Board of Trade's Railway Inspecting Officers, Lt-Col Yolland, recommended that all express and fast trains should have continuous brakes, which should be capable of being applied at a distant signal at Danger (*sic*) by a ramp and contact mechanism. Long before the end of the 19th century several railway companies, but not all, were experimenting with various devices.

Why were they not all doing so? It seems such an obvious development to avoid one of the most common and serious causes of collision, but the railway companies were far from unanimous on the need for any form of technical apparatus at the distant signal, although they were concerned to improve the safety of the signalling system. Some companies held the view that the driver's vigilance might be reduced if he always had the assurance of technical apparatus to intervene should his concentration lapse. Perhaps they were right. Such a view has been held consistently within the industry by some railwaymen. Is it possible that the degree of concentration of an HST driver had been dulled over the many years in which AWS had always been there at his elbow to intervene if necessary? Even after Southall, drivers could be heard to say confidently that they would have taken the train forward from Cardiff just as Driver Harrison did. But such an attitude flies in the face of 150 years' experience of accidents being caused by drivers failing to react to a caution signal in time. The reasons for such failings are immaterial and it is a waste of time attempting to probe the innermost recesses of the driver's mind to find them. It doesn't stop assorted psychologists and others of that ilk trying to do so, of course, but the simple fact is that drivers are human beings and the completely infallible human being does not exist.

The more far-sighted and realistic railway companies continued with their experiments and trials and several of them had developed very good, practical systems by the time World War 1 broke out. Amongst them was the Great Western Railway. It started somewhat later than the others, but ultimately developed the best system of all. It was prompted to do so by a serious accident at Slough, only 10 miles from Southall, on 16 June 1900. The 1.5pm passenger train from Paddington was standing in Slough station when the signalman in Slough East signalbox was asked by the signalman in Dolphin signalbox, a mile to the east, if he could allow an express from Paddington to Falmouth to approach Slough station. As the line in Slough station was occupied by the 1.5pm from Paddington, the signalman in Slough East signalbox replied through his normal block bell signals that the Falmouth express could be allowed to approach only after the driver of that train had been warned that the line in Slough station was already occupied and that he should approach the station cautiously. In order to carry out the cautioning procedures, the signalman at Dolphin maintained all his signals at Danger to stop the Falmouth express, but the driver of that train ignored them and ran past at over 50mph. Even worse, the driver failed to respond to the adverse Distant signal at Slough East and ran into the station at 25/30mph, into collision with the rear of the train already standing there. Five passengers were killed and 35 were seriously injured.

The driver of the Falmouth express was unable to explain his very serious lapse. It is highly unlikely that he would have been able to do so; had he been concentrating he would have seen the signals and responded to them. It was suddenly brought home to the Great Western company that something needed to be done if drivers could inadvertently drive past several signals in such a manner in clear weather and daylight. By 1906, experimental apparatus had been installed on the branch line from Twyford to Henley.

By 1910, contact ramps had been laid at all Distant signals between Paddington and Reading in both directions, and that section of line became one of the safest in the country, at least in Great Western days. The system was also refined to apply the brake if the driver failed to acknowledge the warning. And yet we find, 87 years later, an express train running over that line at 125mph without the benefit of AWS. How could such a thing happen?

After World War 1, the Great Western Railway was the only company to continue to adopt and extend what was called Automatic Train Control (ATC). None of the three other companies formed following the passing of the Railways Act 1921 (the London, Midland & Scottish Railway, the London & North Eastern Railway and the Southern Railway) continued with the experiments and trials of the pre-

A train of loaded stone hopper wagons passes through West Drayton station on 18 February 1987, headed by diesel-electric locomotive No 59002 on the 11.40 Merehead Quarry to Acton. *Brian Morrison*

Grouping companies. The old feeling that drivers were paid to obey signals continued unabated. There were no great public pressures for ATC to be adopted nationwide and the railway companies were in a much more difficult financial position than they had been pre-World War 1. Trade depression in the heavy industries which provided the bulk of their freight revenue, coupled with intense and mainly unchecked road competition, left them with little money for such costly improvements in safety which brought no other benefits.

Nor were there any government pressures; the government was afraid that if it applied such pressures it would be called upon to pay. The companies continued to believe that investment in improved signalling would yield greater benefits, and who is to say that they were wrong? Investment in signalling not only improved safety but also brought considerable benefits in train working. Colour-light signalling allowed drivers to run with greater confidence in darkness and poor visibility. It improved punctuality and increased line capacity. It avoided the need for fogsignalmen, which was both a financial saving and avoided exposing the fogsignalmen to danger at the lineside. ATC provided no other tangible benefit; colour-light signalling won hands down.

After World War 2, but before nationalisation in 1948, the companies said that they saw no prospect of embarking on the installation of ATC owing to the continuing shortage of technical staff and the need to concentrate on overcoming the effects of six years of war and on modernising the signalling system. However, the newly nationalised railways saw a brighter future for the railways in a properly integrated

transport system, and optimistically believed that money would be available for various improvements, including ATC. They therefore embarked on the development of an enhanced ATC of a non-contact type which the LMS had just installed on the London, Tilbury & Southend section, owing to the prevalence of fog there.

This development was prolonged and the system, known as the BR Automatic Warning System (AWS), was not finally approved until November 1956. An allocation of £20 million was included in the British Transport Commission Plan for the Modernisation and Re-equipment of British Railways, issued in 1955. Progress was not very rapid, mainly because to avoid abortive expenditure the installation of AWS was often done concurrently with signalling modernisation. By 1972, 3,000 route miles had been equipped (out of over 10,000 miles on the system as a whole), and by 1985 over 6,300 route miles had been dealt with.

During the whole of this period drivers were having to drive over non-equipped lines at times, and it might be considered anomalous to argue that whilst they were expected to drive safely over non-equipped routes, they could not be expected to do so over an equipped route with the AWS inoperative. And so, for many years it had been accepted that AWS was only an aid to drivers and did not relieve them of

Signal gantry carrying signal No SN280, viewed from Hayes & Harlington station. It displays a double yellow aspect (Preliminary Caution). Driver Harrison on the Swansea– Paddington train failed to react to this signal. The signal on the right-hand side of the gantry is used to control trains passing over the down main line in the up direction. October 2002. *Author*

the responsibility for observing all signals. However, it was realised that it was undesirable to allow trains to run for long periods with the AWS equipment on the train out of service for any reason. Instructions were issued that trains should not enter service (ie from stabling sidings or a maintenance depot) unless the AWS equipment was in working order, but it was still necessary to cater for failures in service.

These failures commonly took the form of an inability to cancel a warning, which caused the brakes to be applied and the train to be immovable. To cater for such a situation, the AWS equipment had an isolation lever which enabled the AWS to be switched out of service (ie isolated) so that the train could be moved. However, it was considered unsatisfactory to allow an 'isolated' train to continue in service all day, and instructions were therefore issued which required it to be taken out of service at the first suitable location, *without causing delay or cancellation*. Therefore, so far as the Rules were concerned, it was in order to run an HST from Cardiff to Paddington at normal speeds with the AWS isolated, because

it was unlikely that the train could be withdrawn from service (ie cancelled) *en route* without causing delay. This might be regarded as very unsatisfactory, but the culture that AWS was only an aid, and was not therefore essential, lived on within BR, and later even within Railtrack.

At one time, HSTs running at over 100mph had two drivers. This was agreed with the drivers' trade union, the Associated Society of Locomotive Engineers & Firemen (ASLEF), and was a sensible precaution because an increase in top speed of 25% was akin to a leap into the unknown. However, experience seemed to indicate that it was unnecessary and the second driver was withdrawn as part of a pay deal. This was the time when the question of running at high speed without the assurance of AWS should have been considered, and a much lower speed limit applied. It was not done. The basic cause of this accident was the railway culture of the time.

The incidental causes

At the beginning of this chapter the incidental causes were dismissed as being largely irrelevant, but they ought to be examined as to their relevance because they occupied a considerable part of the public inquiry when various parties sought to shift the blame elsewhere, or to pillory Railtrack, or to support the driver.

1. The poor alignment of signals preceding the one that was passed at danger

The signal passed at Danger was No SN254. It was preceded by signal No SN270, which was showing one yellow, and, further back, signal No SN280, which was showing two yellows. Arguments were put forward that the driver's view of these signals was less than perfect because one of the beams was misaligned and one of the signals was fixed at a height above normal. However, no evidence was produced that drivers had complained about the sighting of the signals, and whilst they were not entirely in accordance with specification, Professor John Uff, who held the inquiry, concluded (para 3.12) that the signals were adequately visible to a driver keeping a proper lookout. Signal sighting is a complex issue and there are many obstacles to perfection, mainly concerned with obstruction to a long-distance view caused by buildings, bridges, etc interfering with the view around curves, or by the overhead electric line. It is part of a driver's route knowledge to be aware of such signals and take particular care. All drivers know which they are. It is routine.

However, prior to the introduction of the Heathrow Express service the signals concerned had been at eye-level and were well aligned. After the associated resignalling, SN280 was positioned higher than was allowed in the Signalling Standards and the beam of signal SN270 was badly out of focus. Had it been properly focussed it would

The massive signal gantry containing signal No SN254, the signal which was passed at red by Driver Harrison. It is located immediately on the approach to Southall station.
Author

have announced itself to Driver Harrison more forcibly, as did the red aspect at signal SN254 when almost ³/₄ mile away.

2. The routeing of the freight train

One of the problems with public inquiries of the Southall type is that most of the people involved have little or no knowledge of railway operations or technicalities. No experienced railwayman would question the signalman's right to cross a freight train in front of an approaching express passenger train if traffic conditions indicated that it was the correct course of action. The signalman is entitled to act in the belief that drivers will stop at red signals. The railway could not function at all if signalmen had to consider, when they were planning a move, the possibility of a collision. The signalling regulations have been refined over a period of a century and a half, and incorporate all the lessons that have been learned in that period. However, to those who are unacquainted with the art and science of signalling, it perhaps seemed strange that a signalman should act as he did at

Southall. They have this mental picture of the express hurtling to destruction (which of course it did). But would their attitude have changed if the freight train had been another HST? Presumably that would have been acceptable to them. The signalling system is an essential part of the railway and is designed to keep trains apart, ie to prevent them from crashing into each other, and passenger trains frequently encounter red signals, mainly because there is another passenger train in the way.

The idea of a freight train being given precedence over an express passenger train may cause eyebrows to rise. It is another part of railway culture that passenger trains, no matter how humble, must always be given priority over freight trains, no matter how important. But freight trains are no longer the heavily loaded mixed goods of ancient memory, trundling along at 25mph. They are important to the customer, who demands express passenger train standards of performance and is entitled to them. What is more, if he does not get them he will soon take his business elsewhere. Professor Uff spent 10 pages of his report discussing the question. He concluded (para 7.5): 'Any (train) regulation policy must be based on the assumption that trains will comply with signals.'

3. The standard of maintenance at Old Oak Common

The report concludes that the standard of maintenance, testing and repair at Old Oak Common Maintenance Depot was inadequate and states, quite correctly, that if the defective AWS had been repaired the accident would not have happened. But one can say that about many of the myriad events in the Southall accident saga. Accidents are full of 'if onlys', and it is unrealistic to expect that maintenance procedures will always be 100% perfect, even though one should try to make them so. That is not the real world.

4. The passing of verbal messages

The report makes sorry reading indeed about errors and omissions in the passing of verbal messages. Such mistakes cannot be entirely eradicated, but the new problem that emerged in the Southall accident was the split in the Control organisation arising from the privatisation structure. Drivers now report to their own company Control Office, in this case Great Western Trains, whilst signallers report to their company Control Office, Railtrack. This split in the Control Office resulted from the privatisation structure separating the responsibility for signallers from the responsibility for train operators, a fundamental error. Throughout railway history they have been part of the same company and have worked together as part of the same team, under the same Control organisation.

One cannot say for certain that the accident would not have happened in BR days, but it is very likely that the easier and more reliable passing of messages that then existed between signalmen, drivers and one Control Office would have led to effective action being taken at an earlier stage of the story. It cannot be proved, of course, and only an experienced railway operator would recognise the situation. Unfortunately, Professor Uff, despite his considerable attributes, did not have such experience, nor was it brought to his attention.

The nature of public inquiries

From 1871 to 1997 inquiries into railway accidents had been held under the provisions of the Regulation of Railways Act 1871. Sec 3 of that Act gave the Board of Trade powers to appoint any person to be inspector for the purpose of making any inquiry into the cause of any railway accident, and this was the procedure almost always employed. The inspectors so appointed always came from the ranks of the Inspecting Officers of the Board of Trade's (later the Ministry of Transport's) Railway Inspectorate. Although there was no statutory requirement to hold the inquiry in public, it was always the practice to do so. The inspector was required to make a report to the Board of Trade stating the causes of the accident, 'and all the circumstances attending the same, and any observations thereon or on the evidence or on any matters arising out of the investigation which they think right to make to the Board of Trade'. The Board of Trade was required to make the report public 'in such manner as they think expedient'.

Provision existed within the Act for inquiries of a more formal type. Sec 7 of the Act provided that: 'where it appears to the Board of Trade . . . that a more formal investigation of the accident . . . is expedient . . . it may . . . appoint any person possessing legal or special knowledge to assist an inspector'.

Sec 7 also provided that one of a variety of legal persons should hold the inquiry with the assistance of an inspector or other assessor. It then went on to say that such formal investigation should be held in open court.

For a few years after 1871, some inquiries were held under Sec 7 with an inspector being assisted by a legal person, but the practice was soon dropped. Inspectors stated that they had found the legal person to be a nuisance, and prone to ask irrelevant questions.

Inquiries which were held by a legal person were very few. The first was the Tay Bridge collapse in 1879, but for nearly 100 years there were no more. Inspectors' inquiries proved entirely satisfactory, but in 1968 there was a serious accident at Hixon level crossing in Staffordshire when an express passenger train ran into an abnormal load passing at very low speed over a level crossing which was controlled by the relatively new automatic half barriers. There had been some public disquiet about the introduction of such equipment, and because the Highways Department of the Ministry of Transport had been closely involved in establishing the principles of such crossings it was rightly felt that it would be inappropriate for a Railway Inspector to hold the inquiry. It was therefore held under Sec 7 of the 1871 Act by Mr E. B. Gibbens QC.

The next occasion in which a formal investigation was required was in 1987, following a disastrous fire at King's Cross underground station. This also was a reasonable decision because it was not, strictly speaking, a transport accident. However, the use of Sec 7 following the Clapham Junction collision in 1989 was completely unjustified. It was a straightforward railway accident, the cause of which was known within a few hours. The Minister of Transport misguidedly agreed to a 'full public inquiry', which was wrongly interpreted by the Ministry to mean a Sec 7 investigation. An Inspecting Officer's normal public inquiry would have sufficed, and would have avoided the pantomime that followed. The inquiry was held in the huge Westminster Central

Heavily loaded freight trains are now a common sight on Britain's mixed traffic railways. A train load of gypsum is seen approaching Polhill tunnel, between Dunton Green and Knockholt, headed by a Class 60 diesel-electric locomotive, No 60068 *Charles Darwin*, on 20 February 2001. The train is the 11.35 from Mountsorrel (Leics) to Dover Western Docks. *Brian Morrison*

Hall, which was filled with the serried ranks of interested parties, each with its accompanying retinue of legal representatives and advocates. It lasted for an incredible 65 days. The preparation took even longer. The inquiry considered over 13,000 pages of documents.

No more of these Sec 7 inquiries was held before the Southall accident, but an event of considerable impact had just occurred. The Health & Safety Executive (HSE) decided to repeal the 1871 Act and arrange for future public inquiries to be held under the auspices of the Health & Safety at Work etc Act 1974. Inquiries under that Act are normally held in private under Sec 14, but there is provision under the Health & Safety Inquiries (Procedure) Regulations as set out in Statutory Instrument 1975 No SI 335, amended by (Statutory Instrument) SI 1976 No 1246, for a more formal public inquiry of the type held under Sec 7 of the 1871 Act. The HSE therefore issued the Railway Safety (Miscellaneous Provisions) Regulations 1997, which repealed the whole of the 1871 Act (together with other Victorian railway safety legislation). Thenceforth there were only two types of inquiry available to the HSE — a private inquiry, known as a technical investigation, and a full-blown public inquiry guaranteed to last for months, consume tens of thousands of man-hours and cost millions of pounds. The chickens soon came home to roost, with Southall, hotly pursued by Ladbroke Grove. Without such precipitate and unwise action, the HSE would have been able to hold a normal Railway Inspectorate public inquiry into Southall, but that option was no longer available to it and public opinion would not have accepted a private inquiry.

These judicial inquiries closely resemble a court of law. Professor Uff presided rather like a judge, and the prosecution case was presented by the Treasury Solicitor. All the interested parties, of whom there were 11 at the Southall Inquiry, were represented by solicitors and counsel. The cast list is interesting. It consisted of ASLEF, Amey Rail, Angel Train Contracts, British Transport Police (BTP), the Central Rail Users Consultative Committee, EWS, Great Western Trains, HSE, the National Union of Rail, Maritime & Transport (RMT), two passengers' committees, and Railtrack. The witnesses (there are nearly 200 mentioned in the report) were interviewed in turn, then questioned and cross-examined by counsel for each of the interested parties. As can be imagined, this was a very long drawn out process and resulted in many thousands of pages of evidence. It was very thorough but totally unjustified. An old-fashioned Inspecting Officer would have dealt with it in a couple of days at most, and within a few weeks of the accident. It would have avoided the legal tangle which followed.

The course of the inquiry

Professor John Uff QC, FREng was appointed to inquire into this accident with the following terms of reference:

'To determine why the accident happened, and in particular to ascertain the cause or causes, to identify any lessons which have relevance for those with responsibilities for securing railway safety and to make recommendations.'

The inquiry was held between September and December 1999, two years after the accident. The inquiry proceedings actually began in December 1997, with a formal opening in February 1998, but as the driver of the HST was charged with manslaughter in April 1998 and criminal charges were being considered against Great Western Trains no further progress could be made. The course of events then became even more farcical. In December 1998 manslaughter charges and charges under the Health & Safety at Work Act 1974 were brought against the driver of the HST and against Great Western Trains. These criminal proceedings were not resolved until July 1999, leaving the way open for the public inquiry into the accident to resume. Whilst this was going on, the Ladbroke Grove accident occurred.

It may seem odd that two separate prosecutions can be made over one incident, and it became a case of: 'If the police don't get you on criminal charges, the HSE will get you on the Act'. If both prosecutions succeed, the defendant is being punished twice. This may seem somewhat unfair and at variance with the principles of natural justice, but has not raised any storm of protest; in fact no one has been heard to protest at all. Perhaps commentators are bemused by the unreality of the whole affair. Professor Uff, to his credit, was

First Great Western is supplementing its main fleet of High Speed Trains (HSTs) with Class 180s, the 'Adelantes'. Whilst visually striking, the class has had considerable teething troubles. The first one in revenue service, No 180104, is seen at Paddington forming the 11.15 to Bristol Temple Meads on 28 December 2001. *Brian Morrison*

not too happy with it either. His recommendations were published in 2000, approaching three years after the accident, and might almost be considered irrelevant after such a passage of time. Fortunately, the railway authorities did not wait for them and took immediate action where appropriate.

The report

The report, which occupies 226 pages, with an additional 34 pages of appendices, set a challenge to future inquiry chairmen. On the whole it is a good report, well-researched and argued, but unfortunately Professor Uff could not resist becoming mired in the minutiae of the accident when making his recommendations. There are 93 of them. No industry can deal conscientiously and thoroughly with such a mass of recommendations, and the cost of trying to do so is not inconsiderable. Perhaps it will suffice to deal with the important ones.

The vital one is Recommendation No 13, which states bluntly that: 'AWS is to be regarded as vital to the continued running of the train'. However, common sense is still required in the interpretation of this recommendation in case a failure of the AWS were to bring a train to a stand miles from anywhere. It was therefore decided that the Control Office may allow the train to be moved at not more than 40mph to a location where it and its passengers can be satisfactorily dealt with.

Recommendation No 66 states that the ATP should be maintained in a fully operational state. Great Western Trains had already brought this into effect.

Recommendation No 69 makes the very important point that all parties in the industry must ensure that paper-based procedures do not become divorced from reality and should include senior managers maintaining a direct knowledge of the situation in railway workplaces, ie they must know what is going on at the workface. That is an essential part of a manager's job, but so easy to overlook when faced with the pressures and bureaucracy endemic on today's railway. Unfortunately, Professor Uff's 93 recommendations do tend to increase the bureaucratic load and distract managers from their main jobs.

Accident investigations and inquiries

These are dealt with in Recommendations 73 to 85 and have the laudable objective of bringing some clarity and common sense out of the chaos engendered by the fragmented railway system, the heavy-handed involvement of the British Transport Police and the lack of leadership from the HSE. Professor Uff was particularly concerned. He said: 'Accident investigation is not rendered more effective by duplicated and partial procedures. Unregulated and competing interests succeeded in duplicating and confusing both the investigation and inquiry processes.'

Professor Uff states that the primary forum for deciding upon appropriate recommendations following an accident should be the Rail Industry Inquiry, and that nothing should be permitted to delay its opening, nor the completion of its report and recommendations. He also states that HM Railway Inspectorate (HMRI) should control the technical investigation. He does not specifically mention the involvement of the BT Police but his implication is clear — the BT Police should not carry out its own inquiry in parallel, nor should it hinder those whose responsibility it is. The role of the BT Police is dealt with in detail in the body of the report (para 15.23) and it is worth repeating the first few lines verbatim:

'It is unacceptable that a technical accident investigation should be directed or controlled by BTP. Their lack of expertise, and dependency on outside advice, led to most of the (problems). A technical investigation is conducted for reasons much wider than potential prosecution.'

Unfortunately the report was not issued until after the Ladbroke Grove accident, when there appear to have been similar problems.

There is one serious omission from the recommendations, a matter which has been a fundamental factor in every previous accident. Professor Uff does not mention the need for the line to be cleared and the track restored as quickly as possible so that normal working can be resumed with the least possible delay. It does the dead and injured no service to keep the line closed for long periods, and it forces erstwhile rail passengers on to the far more dangerous roads. However, far worse was to come, as the following chapters will show.

The legal proceedings

Great Western Trains was charged with seven separate counts of corporate manslaughter. The HSE also prosecuted Great Western Trains under the Health & Safety at Work Act for failing to ensure that 'the public were not exposed to risks to their health and safety'. However, when the trial was held at the Old Bailey in London, the judge, Mr Justice Scott Baker, ordered that Great Western Trains be acquitted of manslaughter. He ruled that a corporation could be found guilty of manslaughter only if the prosecution could prove that a particular senior executive was grossly negligent. The prosecution did not produce such evidence, and said it would offer no evidence against the driver 'for parity'. So this very expensive trial, which had cost the British Transport Police many thousands of man-hours and diverted police time from the essential policing of railway stations and other railway premises, proved to be largely a waste of time and public funds. The question of why the BT Police embarked on this fruitless course remains unanswered.

However, the HSE prosecution was more successful, because Great Western Trains pleaded guilty and was fined £1,500,000 at a hearing on 27 July 1999. One imagines that by this time GWT was heartily sick of the whole charade and pleaded guilty to avoid wasting any more time. The HSE charge against the driver was dropped at the judge's direction, as no evidence had been presented by the prosecution. So, of the four charges, only one succeeded. Were BTP and the Crown Prosecution Service badly advised and short of expert help? It would appear so. Was the cause of justice truly served by the expense and man-hours involved in these four actions? It would appear not.

A final appraisal of the report

Professor Uff has probed thoroughly and has produced what is on the whole a good, well-balanced report. It is also to his credit that he has not allowed himself to be unduly influenced by expert opinions nor swayed by passenger groups. However, he has unfortunately allowed himself to fall into the trap of attempting to make a recommendation on every issue, great or small, which he could find. This is a serious error, because it ranks the essential with the trivial. It enables the industry to choose which to act upon first and which to relegate to the future. No industry can realistically cope satisfactorily with a large number of recommendations within a reasonable timescale, without diverting attention from activities which are possibly more important. It does not have the resources to do so, nor can it easily obtain them because they are in short supply.

The weighting and implementation of recommendations can only be done by experts in that field. Professor Uff would have needed expert assistance to achieve this ranking, but it is available. The panel of independent accident investigators would have been quite suitable. He should have listed the important recommendations separately and restricted them to no more than 10. He should then have listed the less important but still in his view essential (not more than 10). The remainder should have been shown as desirable, but to be implemented at the industry's discretion. Might one hope that future inquiries will adopt this practice, or is that a hope too far?

⑤ Ladbroke Grove — the big one

BY 1999 railwaymen throughout Britain were beginning to look forward to the end of a decade during which, barring any accidents, fewer passengers had been killed in train accidents than in any previous decade. Only 15 passengers had lost their lives since 1990, during which time the railways had run well over 50 million trains and carried over seven billion passengers. The record in previous decades had not been bad — 51 passengers killed in the 1970s and 75 in the 1980s. But the record in the 1990s far surpassed any previous experience. There had been an incredible period of 1,181 consecutive days between 21 July 1991 and 15 October 1994 in which no passenger had been killed in a train accident. And it had been over two years since the last fatalities at Southall on 19 September 1997. It seemed to indicate firmly that any fears about safety arising from privatisation were largely unfounded.

And yet, 'barring any accidents'. Normally an idiomatic phrase, but railwaymen knew full well that every decade or so there is the 'Big One', and there was no reason why the future should be different. It was merely a question of when. Older railwaymen, whose memories went back prewar, could recite them:

10 December 1937	Castle Cary, LNER (Edinburgh–Glasgow)	35 passengers killed
30 September 1945	Bourne End, LMS (north of Watford)	41 passengers killed
8 October 1952	Harrow & Wealdstone, London Midland Region	108 passengers killed
4 December 1957	St Johns, Lewisham, Southern Region	89 passengers killed
5 November 1967	Hither Green, Southern Region	49 passengers killed
6 July 1978	Taunton, Western Region	12 passengers killed
12 December 1988	Clapham Junction, Southern Region	34 passengers killed

Above left:
Disaster at Nunhead Viaduct, near St Johns, Lewisham, on 4 December 1957, after a driver had passed a signal at Danger in fog and collided with the train in front. Eighty-nine passengers were killed in Britain's second-worst peacetime railway accident. *BR*

Left:
The wreckage of the 19.43 from Hastings to Charing Cross at Hither Green after the derailment on 5 November 1967. *Author's collection*

However, when the Big One finally arrived it was in many ways the worst one since those two big accidents of the 1950s.

Tuesday 5 October 1999

Train No 1K20, a three-car Class 165 'Thames Turbo' diesel multiple-unit, left London Paddington at 08.06 at the start of its routine journey to Bedwyn, three stations beyond Newbury. At the controls sat Driver Michael Hodder. The train threaded its way over the tangle of lines and crossovers in the first two miles and approached a signal at red. That signal subsequently became notorious in every sitting room in the country, achieving its unwelcome fame through the power of television and the daily newspapers. It was signal No SN109. Drivers are expected to stop at signals displaying a red aspect, and the driver of the Bedwyn train had been warned to expect a red aspect at SN109 by a sequence of cautionary signals preceding it.

SN109 was at red because the train's path on to the down main line ahead was not free. That path required the Bedwyn train to cross over the up main line on which a High Speed Train (HST) from Cheltenham to Paddington, train No 1A09, was closely approaching. For whatever reason, the driver of the Bedwyn train did not stop at signal SN109, but actually accelerated past it. Its path ahead eventually took it into direct conflict with the HST and the two trains met head-on at a closing speed estimated to be in the region of 130mph, a record at that time in the history of Britain's railways. The Bedwyn train was partly destroyed by the impact, but the coaches of the HST, shielded from the impact to some extent by the heavy power car at the front of the train, survived remarkably well. However, an old terror reappeared — fire, fed by thousands of gallons of oil fuel. The time was 08.09, the place Ladbroke Grove Junction.

The trains

The 08.06 train from Paddington to Bedwyn was formed by a three-car Class 165/1 diesel multiple-unit, No 165115. It was one of a series built at the York works of British Rail Engineering Ltd and a private firm, ABB, during 1992 and 1993. These were originally known as 'Networker Turbos' in British Rail days, but had subsequently been leased and operated by the Thames Trains Train Operating Company (TOC) and became known as 'Thames Turbos'. The vehicles were fabricated by welding together extruded sections of aluminium. The three-car set weighed 113 tonnes.

The HST was one of a series built in British Railways' workshops between 1976 and 1982. The unit which formed

The broken rail which caused the catastrophic derailment on 5 November 1967 at Hither Green. Forty-nine passengers were killed. *Author's collection*

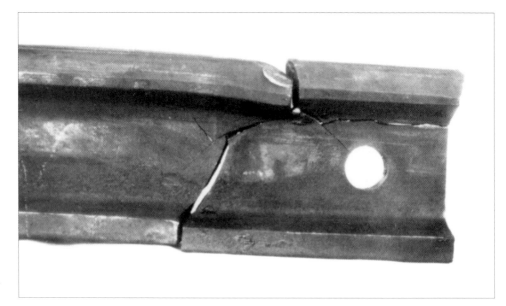

Clearing up after the disastrous collision on 12 December 1988 near Clapham Junction. Thirty-four passengers were killed. *Jeremy de Souza*

Above:
Fire-damaged sleeping cars at Taunton after the fire on 6 July 1978. Twelve passengers lost their lives. *Peter Triggs*

Below:
A Thames Trains Class 165 'Turbo' diesel multiple-unit enters Hayes & Harlington station on 1 October 2002. Thames Trains has a large fleet of these units, one of which was involved in the head-on collision at Ladbroke Grove. They were built by BR Engineering Ltd and ABB at York works in 1992/3. *Author*

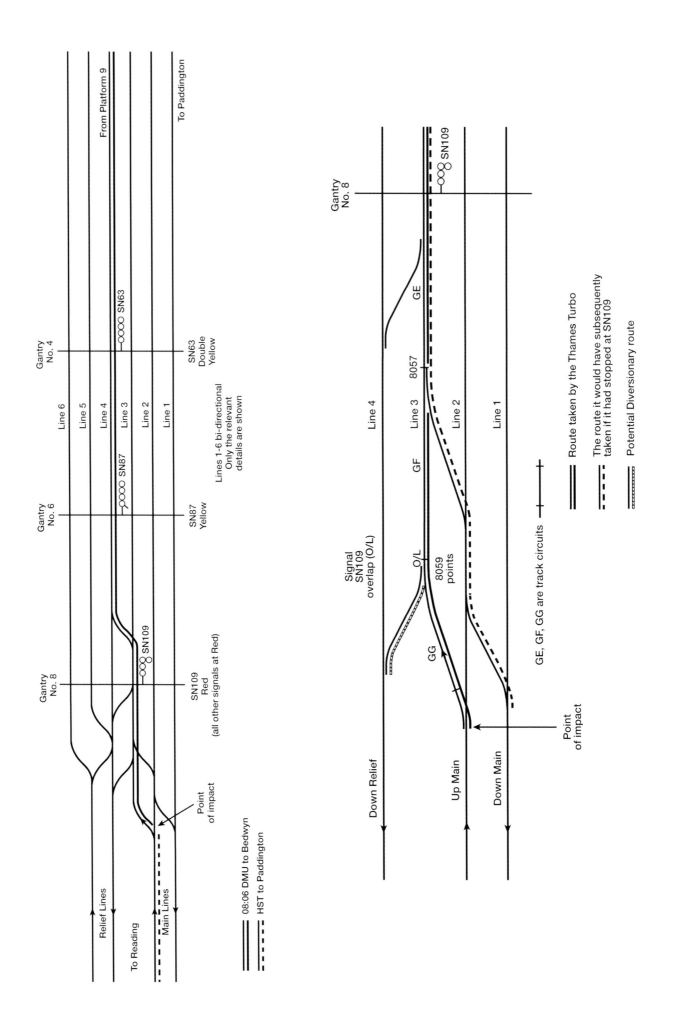

train No 1A09 consisted of eight Mk 3 coaches, with a power car at each end. The coaches were lettered A to H, with coach H leading. Coaches H and G were first class, followed by coach F (the buffet car) and standard class coaches E to A. They were constructed from mild steel. The complete train weighed 435 tonnes.

The track layout

A scheme for a revised track layout between Paddington and Ladbroke Grove was approved by the British Railways Board in 1989. It was designed to accommodate an increased frequency of both main line InterCity trains and Network SouthEast suburban services, together with the proposed services to Heathrow Airport. High-speed connections and crossovers were to be used, allowing trains to reach 100mph two miles from Paddington and cross from one line to another at up to 90mph.

A completely new layout was designed, consisting of six lines from Paddington to Ladbroke Grove, with each line capable of being used in both up and down directions as required. (The up direction is towards Paddington, the down direction is towards Reading and the West.) At Ladbroke Grove the six lines converged into four, the up and down

Far left:
Collision at Ladbroke Grove, 5 October 1999.

Left:
Collision at Ladbroke Grove — the signalling.

Theatre-type route indicators fitted above the signals at the south end of Derby station. The left-hand signal, No DY446, displays an 'S' indication. *BR*

main lines and the up and down relief lines. The six bi-directional lines were called Nos 1 to 6. Line No 1 is on the south side of the layout, line No 6 on the north side.

The signalling

The standard British Railways four-aspect colour-light signalling is in use throughout the area. Each signal has four lenses, vertically arranged. The topmost lens is yellow, the next one down is green, then another yellow, and finally the lowest lens is red. This arrangement of lenses is designed to bring the red lens nearest to the driver's eye level.

The sequence of aspects seen by a driver when a signal ahead is at Danger (showing a red aspect) is as follows:

- The first warning that the driver will receive when a signal ahead is at Danger will be given by a signal displaying two yellow aspects, meaning: 'Preliminary Caution. Proceed, and be prepared to find the next signal displaying one yellow light.'

- This warning will be reinforced at the next signal, which will be displaying one yellow aspect, meaning: 'Caution. Proceed, and be prepared to stop at the next signal.'

A signal displaying two yellows (often referred to as a double

Theatre-type route indicators in use at Leeds before the recent modernisation. 'A' route is denoted by signal No L123. *Author*

yellow) is normally situated at braking distance from one displaying a red aspect. Braking distance is the distance which a train needs in which to come to a stand, using normal braking, from the maximum permitted speed of that section of line. Normal braking is known as full service braking and is the mode of braking normally applied. Emergency braking uses the same equipment, but if the driver selects the emergency braking position of his brake control lever it has the effect of causing the brake to be fully applied slightly more quickly.

The purpose of using two caution signals is to allow trains to follow each other at closer headways (ie intervals) and remain on the move, and is standard practice in busy suburban areas and on busy main lines.

If there is a diverging junction ahead of a signal, information regarding the route which is set is conveyed to the driver in one of two ways. For speeds up to 60mph, the indication may given by the illumination of a letter or number in an indicator box (known as a theatre-type or multi-lamp indicator) corresponding to the route set, eg a figure '1' would indicate Line 1. The letter 'M' would indicate main line. The indicator box may be situated either above the signal aspects or alongside them. The term 'theatre-type indicator' is a long-established but rather old-fashioned reference to the indicators displayed alongside the stage in music halls, on which the number displayed referred to the number of the turn on the programme.

At junctions where drivers would have difficulty in reading a theatre-type indication from a satisfactory distance when approaching at high speed, a different type of indicator is used, known simply as a junction indicator. The route set is indicated by a row of white lights (usually five) inclined to either right or left as appropriate. Usually, no route indication is given if the route is set for the highest-speed route.

Following the rearrangement of tracks referred to above, new signalling was installed and brought into use on 4 January 1993. Signal No SN109 was a standard four-aspect signal, with a standard junction indicator employing a row of white lights mounted on top. The signal was mounted on a gantry which also carried signals for the other five lines. It was envisaged that the maximum permitted speed on the approach to that signal along Line 3 would be 95mph. It was soon discovered that the driver's approach view of SN109 was impaired by a low overbridge, as a result of which the signals were lowered slightly and the red lens was relocated to the left of the lower yellow lens. The five-light junction indicator was replaced by a theatre-type indicator, which was located alongside the signal aspects. The maximum permitted approach speed was reduced to 60mph, which is the maximum speed allowed where theatre-type indicators are employed.

The next sighting problem concerning signal No SN109 (and other signals) was caused by the erection of overhead line electrification equipment for the Heathrow Express service. This was brought into use on 24 November 1996.

There is another form of displaying junction route indications, which was developed in the late 1970s for use on high-speed junctions in order to give the driver early indication of the route ahead that was set and enable him to adjust his speed to the designed speed of the junction. It takes the form of flashing yellow indications, the sequence of signals being as follows:

- Two flashing yellow lights. Meaning: 'Next signal displaying one flashing yellow light'.

- One flashing yellow light. Meaning: 'Be prepared to find the next signal (ie the junction signal) displaying one yellow light with junction indicator for the highest speed diverging route'.

If the line ahead of the junction on the diverging route is clear, the junction signal may clear to a less restrictive aspect in time to avoid the driver reducing speed unnecessarily.

Flashing yellow indications had been installed at Paddington as part of the resignalling, but they were removed in January 1999 because the reduced maximum speeds allowed in the area meant that they were no longer necessary and only added to the complexity of the signalling. Also, a number of cases of drivers passing signals at Danger were attributed to their misinterpreting the flashing aspects.

All the signals concerned were controlled from Slough New signalbox, which will be described later in this chapter.

Automatic Train Protection (ATP), the BR Automatic Warning System (AWS) and the Train Protection & Warning System (TPWS)

1. Automatic Train Protection (ATP)

The history of ATP on Britain's main line railways dates back to the late 1980s, when the British Railways Board decided in November 1988 to adopt an ATP system. The Great Western line out of Paddington was one of two chosen for trials, and contracts for the installation of the equipment were awarded to ACEC Transport in 1990. The trials began in 1991, using HSTs, but were very prolonged, and even by the time of the Southall accident in 1997 the system was not regarded as being sufficiently satisfactory for it to be taken into regular use.

However, after Southall more attention was paid to the maintenance of the ATP equipment and it was brought into full use on Great Western HSTs. Heathrow Express trains were equipped with ATP from the beginning, and it worked satisfactorily. This experience emphasises the difficulty of retrofitting ATP equipment to trains already in service on which no provision had been made for the fitting of ATP. It is perhaps of interest that ATP was not in service on HST train 1A09 on the morning of the accident, but it was of no significance in the accident. All lines are equipped with ATP between Paddington and Ladbroke Grove, but only the main lines are equipped thence to Reading and beyond.

The 'Thames Turbo' fleet was not equipped with ATP. It had not been planned to do so whilst trials were continuing, and during 1994 and 1995 discussions took place between the British Railways Board, the Health & Safety Commission and the Secretary of State for Transport, as a result of which it was decided that there was no reasonable case on cost-effective grounds for adopting ATP.

A typical signal-head arrangement, showing a four-aspect main running signal, together with two junction indicators located above, denoted by the illumination of a row of five white lights. To the left of the signal is a theatre-type junction indicator, used for low-speed junctions. *BR*

Following a collision at Royal Oak on 10 November 1995 involving a 'Thames Turbo' passing a signal at Danger, Thames Trains carried out an investigation to consider whether its trains should be equipped with ATP of the type used by the HSTs. That investigation proved negative. A further investigation was carried out by consultants W. S. Atkins following the Southall accident, which still proved negative. Atkins reported: 'From this analysis it is not possible to make a case in cost-benefit terms for installing ATP on sections of route over which Thames Trains operate and for equipping the Thames Trains' fleet of rolling stock with ATP.'

One other factor which has to be borne in mind is that the new Train Protection & Warning System (TPWS) was being developed during this period, the implementation of which was expected within a relatively short time. Unfortunately, development work was prolonged, although trains operated by the Thames Trains company have now been equipped. In addition, track apparatus in the Paddington area has also been installed.

2. The BR Automatic Warning System (AWS)

The use of AWS on British Railways dates back to the 1950s, and all main lines were equipped with it progressively over the next several decades. AWS is installed at all signals in the Paddington area and takes the form of a permanent magnet and an electro-magnet fixed in the 'four-foot' between the rails about 200yd on the approach to a signal. A receiver is fixed underneath the traction unit and reacts to the magnets fixed in the track. A bell and a horn (or an electronic representation) are provided in the cab, together with an acknowledgement button and a visual indicator.

When a signal displays a green aspect (meaning 'the line ahead is clear') the electro-magnet is energised. This causes the bell in the driving cab to give a short ring, and the visual indicator to show all black. No action is required by the driver. With all other signal aspects the electro-magnet is inoperative. When a traction unit passes over the permanent magnet the horn will sound a warning and, unless the driver presses the acknowledgement button within two or three seconds (which will silence the horn), the brakes will be fully applied. When the driver presses the button to acknowledge a warning the visual indicator will display segmented yellow and black to remind him that he has done so.

The vital implication of the word 'warning' in the name of the system is clear — it is a warning to the driver that he needs to apply the brakes. The system itself does not do so once the driver has pressed the button. The action of pressing the button is an acknowledgement of the fact by the driver that he himself has taken over the responsibility for applying the brakes. It might be considered virtually impossible for a situation to arise in which the driver presses the acknowledgement button and then forgets to apply the brake, but such instances do occur from time to time. This appears not to have been the case at Ladbroke Grove. The balance of the evidence seems to indicate that the driver certainly acknowledged the warnings at the two Caution signals preceding signal SN109. He then applied power just before reaching the AWS magnets for signal SN109, acknowledged the warning at the magnets but failed to brake, and continued accelerating past them and the signal itself as though he had received a Proceed indication at the signal (ie either two yellows or one yellow). One of the shortcomings of AWS is that the same warning is given for a signal at red, one yellow or two yellows. In other words, the warning horn gives two contradictory messages — (1) You must stop here, or (2) Proceed past but look out for a Danger signal ahead somewhere. That has always been one of the unsatisfactory features of AWS. On the day in question, signalling data is said to prove that SN109 was showing red.

3. The Train Protection & Warning System (TPWS)

As mentioned above, this system was designed as a more cost-effective protection system than ATP, and set out to overcome the weakness of AWS in which the driver acknowledges the AWS warning and then fails to apply the brake for any reason. It does so by checking the speed of a train approaching a Stop signal. If the train is approaching too fast to be able to stop at the signal, the brakes will be applied automatically irrespective of anything the driver might or might not do. The equipment does not ensure that the train will stop before the signal but it has the capability to stop, within the safety overlap beyond the signal, a train which is approaching at up to 75mph. It is also important

TPWS grids which form the speed trap. *Author*

A Class 332 'Heathrow Express' electric multiple-unit awaits departure at Paddington on 15 July 2002. The line from Paddington to Heathrow Airport was electrified to serve these trains, but the overhead structures caused some problems with the drivers' view of the signals in the area between Paddington and Ladbroke Grove. *Author*

to understand that TPWS is an overlay to AWS, which will continue in use as now.

The basic TPWS system, known as TPWS–A, consists of an overspeed sensor situated on the track between the two rails about 400yd before a signal. It has two loops (which look like grids). The first loop is the 'arming' loop, operating at a specific frequency, which starts a timer on the train. This is followed by a 'trigger' loop, operating at a different frequency. If the trigger loop is reached before the timer has completed its sequence (about one second for passenger trains), it indicates excessive speed and the brakes will be applied.

TPWS also incorporates a 'Train Stop' at a signal. It is energised when the signal is at Danger and will cause an immediate brake application at any speed if the signal is passed when at Danger. This is a very valuable additional safeguard, as instances continue to arise when signals at the end of station platforms are wrongly passed at Danger.

A further development consists of TPWS+ to provide for trains approaching at more than 75mph. An additional overspeed sensor, placed about half a mile before a signal, is said to be able to offer full protection for trains approaching at up to 100mph. Trials are also being conducted to deal with trains approaching at speeds up to 25mph, by applying special controls to the signal approaching the one at danger.

The history of occasions on which signal SN109 had been passed at danger

Signal SN109 had been wrongly passed at Danger on eight occasions between 1993 and the date of the Ladbroke Grove collision. This was considered excessive, although no evidence was produced at the inquiry of the frequency with which trains approach the signal at Danger and stop there safely, which would have enabled the failure rate to be calculated.

A number of interesting facts emerged. All the SPADs (Signals Passed at Danger) occurred between 08.00 and 09.30 or between 17.00 and 19.00. Three of them occurred between 08.00 and 09.30, all in daylight, and five in the evening period, two of which were at dusk. Is there any significance in the fact that two occurred at almost exactly the same time as the Ladbroke Grove accident, on 13 February 1995 (105yd) and 3 April 1997 (72yd)? However, the angle of the sun would have been different on those three dates, so that would not have been a common factor.

Four of the SPADs involved very short overruns of less then 15yd, which is less than the length of an engine. The actual distances were 2yd, 3yd, 11yd and 14yd. It also indicates that the driver knew that the signal was at Danger and was already braking to stop at it but had commenced to brake a second too late or that he had misjudged his braking in the last few yards. In no case was there any danger, and in only one of the eight cases did the train fail to stop within the safety overlap. The overruns of more than 15yd were as follows:

- 13 February 1995 at 08.10. Overrun 105yd. The driver read the wrong signal on the SN109 gantry as applying to him and did not realise his mistake until he was close to SN109 signal.

- 15 March 1996 at 18.58. Overrun 146yd. It was considered that the driver had lost concentration when approaching SN109 and braked late.

- 3 April 1997 at 08.12. Overrun 72yd. The driver appears to have failed to see the signal preceding SN109 and was late braking in consequence.

- 4 February 1998 at 17.18. Overrun 432yd. The flashing junction signalling appears to have caused some confusion and the driver was quite near SN109, travelling at about 60mph, when he saw it was at red.

The detailed progress of the Paddington to Bedwyn train up to the point of collision

The train departed from Platform 9 and passed signal SN17 at the platform end at green. It was routed on to Line 4. The driver had accelerated to 40mph when he passed the next signal, SN43, which was also at green. He continued along Line 4 to the next signal, SN63, which was showing double yellow. His speed had reached 46mph and he braked to 40mph.

He continued along Line 4 and passed the next signal, SN87, at 40mph. It was showing single yellow with junction indicator to Line 3 leading up to SN109. He passed through the crossover on to Line 3 at about 37mph and immediately applied power just before receiving the AWS warning for SN109, which was at red.

He continued to accelerate past SN109 and beyond, reaching 51mph. He applied the brakes just before the collision.

The damage to the trains

The HST and the 'Thames Turbo' met head-on at a closing speed of about 130mph in one of the most horrifying acci-

A graphic photograph showing the devastation at Ladbroke Grove following the head-on collision between a three-car 'Thames Turbo' diesel multiple-unit and a First Great Western High Speed Train on Monday 4 October 1999. The front car of the DMU was almost totally destroyed in the collision, which occurred at a closing speed in the region of 130mph, the highest in British railway history up to that time (it was surpassed by the collision at Great Heck, described in Chapter 12). The rear coaches of the HST survived remarkably well.
Modern Railways

dents since the 1950s. The HST had been travelling at about 80mph and the 'Thames Turbo' at 51mph. Such an awful impact proved to be very destructive and was accompanied by considerable loss of life.

The Mk 3 coaches of HSTs have had an excellent history of maintaining their structural integrity in collisions and derailments, and this accident was no exception, even though the front coaches of the train were thrown around. Coach H, the leading coach, jack-knifed and the next two coaches, G and F, toppled over on to their sides and slid along until they came to rest. It was considered that the crash performance of the Mk 3 body shell in this accident had been excellent — a tribute to its builders and designers.

The 'Thames Turbo' bodyshells were constructed of welded aluminium extrusions. The front car was almost totally destroyed owing to failure along the welded connections. The 'Turbos' met the structural requirements of the time when they were built, several years earlier, but they were not designed to withstand a 130mph head-on collision with the much heavier and stronger 70-tonne power car of an HST. It was no contest. The HST weighed 435 tonnes in total, whilst the entire 'Turbo' weighed a mere 113 tonnes.

The centre car of the 'Turbo' was pushed backwards off the track and was badly damaged, both by compressive pressures from the leading coach and by the HST scraping along its side. The rear car fell on to its side. However, the protection of passengers in the centre and rear cars was considered to be reasonably good, since only one passenger was thrown out by the impact and damage to the bodyshell.

The fire

One of the most disturbing features of this accident was the reappearance of fire as a cause of casualties following an accident. It had been many, many years since fire following a

collision had caused loss of life; in fact one has to go back to the Charfield collision on 13 October 1928 to find such an event. In the intervening 71 years railway carriage design and construction, and the materials used, have improved considerably from the points of view of crash-worthiness and fire-resistance.

At the instant of the collision the fuel tank of the front car of the 'Turbo', located just behind the front bogie, disintegrated after being struck by the bogie, and its diesel fuel escaped under pressure in a finely dispersed mist. The fuel tanks underneath the centre and rear cars were ruptured a few seconds later during the process of being derailed and overturned, causing the fuel to drain from them.

The power car of the HST carried two tanks. One of them was penetrated by the floor section of the 'Turbo' and released fuel under pressure. The other tank was holed in numerous places but released its fuel more slowly.

Immediately after the collision the fuel ignited in a ball of fire about 75yd wide, accompanied by thick, black smoke. The HST was still moving forward owing to its momentum and virtually the whole of the train passed through the fireball in a few seconds. However, the fire did not penetrate the interior of the coaches except for the leading coach, coach H. The fireball entered that coach from the rear and travelled very rapidly halfway along the coach. However, all the passengers except one managed to escape before fire engulfed it, although many were badly burned. The coach was burnt out within about 30 minutes. There were also many trackside fires.

The source of fuel for the fireball was finely dispersed diesel fuel, and much of it came from the contents of the fuel tank of the front car of the 'Turbo', which contained about 150 gallons at the time of the crash. The two fuel tanks of the leading power car of the HST contained over 900 gallons of diesel fuel and contributed to the fires.

The casualties

On the HST

There were 422 passengers and staff on the HST. The driver was killed immediately, together with six passengers who were all travelling in the leading coach, coach H. Five of these passengers were killed by the force of the collision. They had all been in the front end of the coach. The sixth passenger died as the result of inhaling fire fumes but had also sustained significant head injuries which may in themselves have proved fatal. All the remaining 30 passengers were injured, some being very severely burnt.

There were no other fatalities in the remainder of the train, although there were many injuries of varying severity. The details are:

Coach G	42 passengers	40 injured
Coach F	30 passengers and	
(Buffet car)	two catering staff	28 injured
Coach E	85 passengers	56 injured
Coach D	74 passengers	52 injured
Coach C	64 passengers	41 injured
Coach B	40 passengers	23 injured
Coach A	47 passengers and guard	29 injured
(Guard's compartment)		

Once again the Mk 3 coaches of the HST had demonstrated their remarkable protection against fatal injury, even in such a high-speed crash.

The 'Thames Turbo'

There were 25 passengers in the front car. Nineteen of them were killed, together with the driver. All six surviving passengers sustained injuries.

In the centre car there were 60 passengers, of whom three were killed. Almost all the others were injured.

In the rear car there were 62 passengers. One was killed, whose death resulted from traumatic asphyxiation. Only four passengers survived physically unscathed.

Although the 'Turbo' was very badly damaged and provided less protection to passengers than the HST, 20 of the 24 fatalities were in the front car, which was almost completely destroyed. However, of the 124 survivors, only six were uninjured, which is a remarkably high casualty list. Unfortunately, the official accident report does not distinguish between minor and major injuries, as has been the custom, and this distorts the figures, making it impossible to have a fuller appreciation of the results of the accident. For example, the report into the Clapham Junction collision on 12 December 1988 states that 'nearly 500 passengers were injured, 69 of them seriously'. Using the same proportions for the Ladbroke Grove accident, the result would have been '417 passengers and staff were injured, 56 of them seriously'.

Despite the awful fire, only one passenger died from the effect of burns. He had been travelling in the front car of the 'Turbo'. There was also one fatality from inhalation of hot gases. But it would be instructive to know how many of the seriously injured suffered from severe burns.

The history of track and signalling developments in the area after 1990

Phase 1 of the modernisation scheme of track and signalling in the Paddington area was brought into use on 4 January 1993. The extent to which an overbridge obstructed the approach view of the signals on Gantry 8 (which included signal No SN109) had apparently not been realised until the new signalling was brought into use. As a temporary expedient maximum permitted speeds on all lines approaching that gantry from Paddington were lowered to 40mph. On 7 August 1994 a revised arrangement was brought into use, in which the red aspect was removed from the vertical arrangement of aspects and placed alongside and to the left of the lowest aspect of the remaining three. The position-light junction indicators were replaced by theatre-type indicator boxes. The maximum permitted speed was then increased to 60mph.

Erection of steelwork for the 25kV overhead electrification (OHLE) scheme began, and energisation took place on 24 October 1996. The effect was to further reduce the visibility of signals, especially those on Gantries 3 and 8. The insulators used were very much larger and more robust than those used in other OHLE schemes, in order to resist vandalism. On 24 May 1998 the operation of the Heathrow Express began.

Drivers found that the use of the automatic route-setting system (ARS) in conjunction with the new track system

The interior of an Integrated Electronic Control Centre (IECC). *IAL*

containing six lines, all of them bi-directional, meant that there was a multiplicity of routes for trains to follow. One consequence was that the driver's view of the signals ahead would change as he switched from one line to another. The effect of curvature of the route was that a signal would not remain in the same place in the driver's view but would become offset to one side or the other. Many drivers gave evidence to the inquiry that the sighting of signals in the area was difficult and confusing, due to their being intermittently obscured by bridges and the OHLE.

Slough New signalbox, and radio

Slough New signalbox, known as an Integrated Electronic Control Centre (IECC), was commissioned in July 1993. The control room had three workstations, containing a number of VDUs, control buttons, radio equipment, telephones, a tracker ball and keyboard for entering commands. The signaller was able to monitor the operation of the ARS and the movement of trains by observation of the layout displayed on the appropriate VDU screen. He could replace a signal to Danger by using the tracker ball to move its cursor to that signal and pressing a red 'cancel' button. As an alternative he could use the keyboard, but that was slower. The signalman could, if he wished, switch off the ARS and set routes himself.

In the event of a signal being passed at Danger an alarm would sound in the control room and a red alarm would appear on a VDU screen. The same audible alarm also served to give warning of a number of types of malfunction.

Two types of radio system were fitted to trains operating in the area. Trains operated by the Great Western and Virgin companies were equipped with National Radio Network (NRN) apparatus. This system was designed to provide radio contact from the driver to a number of places, including signalboxes. However, the signaller could not contact a driver directly. This would have had to be done through Swindon Control, which could then send out an area message which would be broadcast in the driving cabs of all trains in that area. It should be pointed out that NRN had not been provided originally for driver/signaller communication but had been adapted subsequently within the limits of the system to provide what was a rather cumbersome means of achieving such communication.

The trains operated by Thames Trains and Heathrow Express were equipped with Cab Secure Radio (CSR). This was a tailor-made, superior system designed to allow the operation of trains without guards, known as Driver-only Operation (DOO), but subsequently applied to other trains in the area. It has a range of facilities for driver/signaller communication. The signaller can make a call to a driver, which the driver will receive as soon as he picks up his handset. The signaller can send a Stop message, and can broadcast a call to the cabs of all trains, which will be heard immediately. The driver can speak to the signaller, and he can initiate an emergency call which the signaller would receive and answer immediately. The system also has other facilities which are not relevant to the Ladbroke Grove accident.

The sequence of events after the 'Thames Turbo' passed Signal SN109 was as follows, using zero time when the SPAD alarm sounded in the Slough IECC:

00 seconds	SPAD alarm sounded when the front of the train occupied track circuit GE beyond signal SN109.
05 seconds	A second alarm sounded when the rear of the train cleared the track circuit before signal SN109.
07 seconds	A third alarm sounded when the front of the train occupied the next track circuit GF.
12 seconds	The rear of the train cleared track circuit GE.
18-20 seconds	The signaller replaced signal SN120 to red to attempt to stop the HST.
20 seconds	An alarm sounded as the next track circuit GG became occupied by the 'Thames Turbo'.
26 seconds	Track circuit FZ beyond signal SN120 became occupied by the front of the HST.
33 seconds	The collision occurred.

The actions of the signallers, and the relevant instructions, will be discussed in the next chapter.

❻ Ladbroke Grove — what went wrong?

The public inquiry

Public inquiries are very formal and judicial affairs, held by eminent persons in the legal field. The Rt Hon Lord Cullen PC was appointed on 8 October 1999 by the Health & Safety Commission (HSC), with the consent of the Deputy Prime Minister, John Prescott, to conduct a public inquiry under Sec 14 (2)(b) of the Health & Safety at Work Act 1974. His terms of reference were as follows:

1. To inquire into, and draw lessons from, the accident near Paddington station on 5 October 1999, taking account of the findings of the HSE's investigations into immediate causes.

2. To consider general experience derived from relevant accidents on the railway since the Hidden Inquiry, with a view to drawing conclusions about:
   a) factors which affect safety management
   b) the appropriateness of the current regulatory regime.

3. In the light of the above, to make recommendations for improving safety on the future railway.

(Note — the Hidden Inquiry was concerned with the collision at Clapham Junction in 1988.)

Lord Cullen decided that he would hold the inquiry in two parts, dealing respectively with parts 1 and 2 of the terms of reference. They became known as Ladbroke Grove Rail Inquiry Part 1 (LGRI-1) and Ladbroke Grove Rail Inquiry Part 2 (LGRI-2). In addition, the public inquiry into the collision at Southall on 19 September 1997 (see previous chapter), conducted by Professor John Uff QC, was still proceeding and it was clear that there were a number of issues of common concern to both inquiries. Both accidents occurred when a signal was passed at Danger, now known universally as a SPAD. In the circumstances Lord Cullen and Professor Uff were appointed to chair a separate public inquiry into those common issues, which were:

1. Train Protection & Warning Systems

2. The future application of Automatic Train Protection Systems;

3. SPAD prevention measures.

LGRI-2 and the Joint Inquiry will be dealt with in later chapters.

To assist him in his work as chairman, Lord Cullen chose the following: Professor Peter H. McKie CBE, former Chairman of DuPont (UK) Ltd, and Mr Malcolm J. Southgate, former Deputy Managing Director of Eurostar (UK) Ltd.

Although the report does not say so, Malcolm Southgate had been a career railwayman who rose to become Director of Operations at British Railways Board HQ.

The inquiry was conducted on the same judicial lines as the Southall Inquiry. Counsel to the inquiry, Mr Robert Owen QC, presented the evidence of each witness in turn, and this was followed by cross-examination of the witness by a legal representative of each of the parties represented at the inquiry. The parties were:

The Ladbroke Grove Solicitors' Group, comprising 54 firms of solicitors, representing 168 bereaved and injured;
Collins Passengers' Group, representing 78 bereaved and injured;
The Associated Society of Locomotive Engineers & Firemen;
Thames Trains Train Operating Company;
First Great Western Train Operating Company;
Railtrack;
Rail Users' Consultative Committees;
Health & Safety Commission and Health & Safety Executive;
British Transport Police;
Amey Rail;
Angel Train Contracts Ltd (now Angel Trains Ltd);
Adtranz;
National Union of Rail, Maritime & Transport Workers.
Transport Salaried Staffs' Association;
W. S. Atkins Consultants Ltd (days 50 and 51 only).

Over 100 lay witnesses and 21 expert witnesses gave oral evidence, and a similar number gave written evidence. As can be imagined, the proceedings were extremely prolonged, with each witness being cross-examined in turn by whichever party wished to do so. The amount of paper generated was truly colossal and the ring-binder files were numbered in hundreds. It has to be said that the inquiry was very thorough.

The public inquiry began on 10 May 2000 and closed on 28 September 2000. The report was published on 20 June 2001. It occupies, with appendices, 271 pages and contains 89 recommendations. Some are eminently desirable, but at the other end of the scale some border on the trivial.

The main issues facing the inquiry

The main issues which Lord Cullen had to consider were as follows:

The signalling;
The track layout and flank protection;

The driver and his training;
What caused the driver to pass SN109 signal;
The actions of the signallers;
HMRI's involvement;
Crashworthiness of the coaches;
Fire, and the evacuation of the trains.

A factual description of each of these issues was given in the preceding chapter. This chapter will discuss the issues and Lord Cullen's recommendations.

The signalling

The report reveals a sorry story of vacillation over several years on the part of Railtrack in responding to complaints from drivers and Great Western Trains about the bad sighting of signals, especially those on Gantry 8. Signal No SN109 was one of the signals on that gantry. Lord Cullen describes it as 'institutional paralysis'. Experienced drivers regarded the track layout and the signalling in the Paddington area as very complex, requiring great care.

There was a lack of will on Railtrack's part to do anything positive and an obvious desire not to incur heavy expendi-

ture. The only practical solution would have been to move Gantry 8 to the approach side of the overbridge which partially obscured its signals, but that would have been very expensive, time-consuming and would have had a serious impact on the ability to run the train service whilst the change was being made. It would have required a very strong and determined will to achieve it, and the will and determination were not there. It is also possible that Railtrack was influenced by the development of the Train Protection & Warning System and did not wish to incur heavy expenditure which it might have felt would soon be unnecessary. It may have considered that the timescale required for such a major alteration to signalling in the area to be commissioned would probably be similar to the timescale for TPWS to be installed. TPWS does not make signal sighting any easier but it provides a better second line of defence than AWS.

Railtrack was the party at fault, but it inherited the signalling from BR and was not responsible for drivers. Drivers' complaints about the signalling went to the Train Operating Companies, especially Great Western Trains. Regrettably, no Signal Sighting Committee meeting was held to review the effect on signal sighting of the overhead electrification structures, nor was one carried out following a series of SPADs at signal No SN109. But it is interesting to consider whether, if privatisation had not taken place, BR would have radically altered the signalling at great expense in order to create satisfactory sighting. The question is open to considerable doubt that it would have done so. BR also suffered from an institutional inertia which had been endemic, due partly to the long life of fixed assets and rolling stock. BR was also

A photograph taken on 25 September 1972 showing the massive overbridges which span the tangle of lines outside Paddington station. Most things in the view have changed or disappeared in the intervening 30 years but the bridges remain. The simplicity of the signalling at the extreme left of the picture is noteworthy. *Brian Morrison*

In this view, the camera was positioned immediately above the red aspect of SN109 looking towards Paddington. A 200mm telephoto lens was used to magnify the detail. SN109 applies to Line 3, which is the third from the right. The extent to which the large OHLE insulators and Portobello Bridge obstruct the driver's view of SN109 is evident. *Steve Wilkins*

short of money, a situation that did not apply to Railtrack to the same degree.

On the evidence, one cannot quarrel with Lord Cullen's severe criticisms of Railtrack, among which is: 'a serious and persistent failure to deal with the recognised problem of SPADs in the Paddington area in a prompt, proactive and effective manner'. However, one rather regrets his failure to explore the circumstances that led to Railtrack's lack of effective action, rather than simply to deplore it. Perhaps he was concerned that it would lead him into an examination of the management policies of Railtrack and its culture. That could have been very revealing and rewarding.

An illustration of flank protection. If a train passes signal No 1 at Danger when a route is set to allow a train to travel from 'C' to 'B', it will be diverted out of harm's way at a double junction.

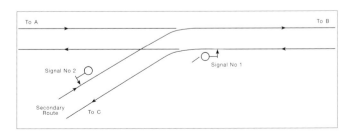

Lord Cullen recommended a thorough risk analysis of the signalling and track layout in the Paddington area to the satisfaction of HM Railway Inspectorate. He also recommended that consideration be given to the installation of an additional gantry to the east of Portobello Bridge for carrying the down direction signals previously carried on Gantry 8.

The track layout and flank protection

In the aftermath of the crash a number of temporary measures were taken. Signal SN109 was taken out of use and Line 3 became an up direction line only. A speed limit of 40mph was imposed on all down trains for just over two miles from Paddington station to beyond Ladbroke Grove Junction, subsequently increased to 50mph from Westbourne Park outwards.

There was much discussion about the question of flank protection beyond signal SN109. None was provided because the Group Standards did not require it. In the absence of flank protection the normal position of facing points directed a train towards the up main line, with the obvious risk of a high-speed head-on collision in the event of a serious SPAD at SN109. Flank protection could have been provided through Points 8059 several hundred yards beyond signal SN109, but that would have diverted a train on to the down relief line, with a risk of a sidelong collision. However, such a collision would have required the runaway train to pass on to the down relief line at precisely the same moment as a train legitimately proceeding along it, which seems unlikely. It also seems preferable to the much greater certainty of a head-on collision with a train on the up main line, but Lord Cullen was lukewarm on the question, merely listing it as a possible measure.

Class 47 diesel-electric locomotive No 47220 gets the road through Doncaster with a loaded merry-go-round working, whilst signalling technicians work on a nearby signal gantry. It is estimated that 80% of the costs of signal maintenance are labour costs and overheads. The use of fibre-optic and LED signals will greatly reduce the amount of maintenance needed. Fibre-optic signals are now in use between Paddington and Ladbroke Grove and on a gantry at Leeds. Signal R53 at Reading has been fitted with LEDs, and trials with them are being conducted on the Chiltern line. *John E. Oxley*

There was also discussion on the question of trap points being provided at the end of Line 3 to derail a runaway train. However, such a derailment, possibly at fairly high speed, might well result in wreckage obstructing the up main line or the down main line, or both. It would not be a suitable solution in this case, nor did Lord Cullen recommend it, but it did raise once more the question of the provision of facing trap points where one line terminates and joins another. Recent practice has been not to provide trap points, and TPWS should reduce the need to do so, whilst ERTMS will avoid it altogether.

The driver and his training

Michael Hodder, the driver of the 'Thames Turbo', was recruited in February 1999. Prior to November 1998 Thames Trains had recruited its drivers internally, but as the supply of candidates diminished it was necessary to recruit potential drivers from other than railway employees. Hodder joined the second phase of recruitment. Thames Trains had 420 applicants, of whom 132 were invited for interview. Hodder was interviewed on 27 November 1998 and assessed to be in the top two of the 132 applicants.

His training was loosely based on the BR system and included four weeks' traction training and 16 weeks' practical handling. The time needed was based on the limited traction and fairly limited route knowledge required by Thames Trains' drivers. Hodder was a good pupil and was highly regarded by his instructors. The report suggests that the special difficulties in the Paddington area were not sufficiently emphasised, but it was difficult to provide proof either way. However, it seems inconceivable that during his many training runs into and from Paddington the problems of signal sighting and the need for special care were not stressed with him, but Lord Cullen, being a lawyer, was looking for evidence, not probabilities.

Hodder had 250 hours of practical instruction and passed out as a driver on 22 September 1999. He drove out of Paddington on 20 occasions between then and the date of the accident. Lord Cullen states bluntly that Driver Hodder's training was not adequate for the task for which he was being prepared, but that raises the question of just how much training should he have had to enable him to see a signal and obey it when he has been warned at the previous signal to expect it to be at red. On what evidence did Cullen base his assertion that training was inadequate? One would not expect a lawyer to make such a statement without evidence, but none was produced. It is very difficult to prove that a certain level of training is adequate or, alternatively, inadequate. The report acknowledges that:

'the immediate cause of the collision was that driver Hodder did not stop at Signal SN109 or attempt to stop thereafter until the crash was imminent. He passed SN109 at red and when . . . no route was indicated for his train. He had passed SN63 at double yellow and SN87 at single yellow. In each case he cancelled the AWS horn which sounded before he reached the signal.'

What might have caused Driver Hodder to pass signal SN109 at danger?

The report considers in great detail the possible reasons why Driver Hodder passed signal SN109 at red and concludes that he must have believed that he had a Proceed aspect. It is difficult to conclude otherwise. He would hardly have gone past the signal without stopping if he believed that it was at red. What is significant is that he did not brake after passing signal SN87 at single yellow but more or less coasted along at 40mph as though it had been at double yellow. There is a theory that the early morning sun low in the sky and immediately behind him may have caused a 'phantom' reflection to appear on the signal head, leading him to read it as a double yellow, but the phenomenon was not observed from a test train at the same time the following day. The theory goes on to suggest that the same circumstance may have occurred at SN109, leading him to read that signal also as a double yellow, but whilst observations from the test train did reveal a diminution of the brightness of the red aspect owing to the sun, it did not produce strong phantom reflections from the yellow lenses. However, the way that Hodder drove, as revealed by the printout from the On-train Monitoring & Recording Equipment, lends credence to the view that he

The photograph above and those on the next two pages illustrate the sequence of signals seen by Driver Hodder as he left Paddington and proceeded towards Ladbroke Grove.
All photographs by Steve Wilkins

Driver Hodder was travelling along Line 4 towards Gantry 4, and the signal applicable to his train, SN63, is fourth from the left and displaying a double yellow aspect (Preliminary Caution — the next signal in the distance is displaying one yellow aspect). The photograph was taken at ground level.

Above:
Approaching gantry No 6 Driver Hodder is still proceeding along Line 4. The signal applicable to his train, SN87, is showing a single yellow aspect with a junction indicator showing that the points ahead are set to divert his train from Line 4 to Line 3. The single yellow aspect is a warning that the next signal is at red and he must be prepared to stop at it. The photograph was taken at ground level.

Below:
Gantry 8 comes into view beneath the overbridge, but the driver's view of the signal aspects up to this point has been partly obstructed by overhead line insulators. All the signals on the gantry are showing red. The train has passed through the crossover from Line 4 to Line 3, and the AWS magnet for signal SN109 is immediately in front of the train. Unfortunately, the magnet will give the same warning whether the signal is displaying two yellows, one yellow, or red and has the potential to mislead the driver. This is the loophole in the AWS system which TPWS is designed to block. This photograph was taken from the driver's position in a Class 165 unit on Line 3, and from here onwards the driver's view of the red aspect of signal SN109 is unobstructed.

Above:
The train now approaches Gantry 8 along Line 3. Signal SN109 is immediately ahead and is showing red, as are all the other signals on the gantry. The photograph was taken from the driver's position in a Class 165 unit under conditions of very bright sunlight at 8.51am on 6 October 1999. The tendency of the sunlight to swamp the lit aspects is evident. The large insulator which obscures the red aspect of SN109 at longer ranges can be seen above and to the left of the signal.

Below:
Signal SN109 as seen from the driver's position in a Class 165 unit on Line 3 at a distance of 17 metres from the gantry. This photograph was taken under conditions of very bright sunlight at 8.50am on 6 October 1999. 'Swamping' of the aspects is evident, but at no time from 8.4am that morning was there evidence of a phantom aspect in any of the aspects on any of the signals on Gantry 8.

The LED signal R53 at Reading, with junction indicator illuminated. *Author*

Below:
Fibre-optic signals.

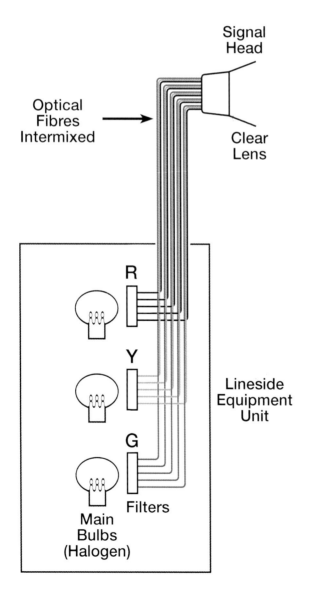

Signal Head

Optical Fibres Intermixed →

Clear Lens

R

Y

Lineside Equipment Unit

G

Filters

Main Bulbs (Halogen)

thought that both SN87 and SN109 were exhibiting double yellow aspects. Otherwise, why should he approach SN109 at what might be regarded as rather excessive speed, and why did he accelerate before reaching SN109?

So-called 'phantom' aspects or 'ghosting' have long been known about. No trials have ever been able to produce a phantom aspect that was as bright as the normal aspect, but the phantom effect can also cause a diminishing of the intensity of the aspect being displayed. It is unlikely that a phantom aspect would deceive an experienced driver, but it is at least less unlikely that an inexperienced driver such as Hodder could be. If there was any ghosting it would affect both yellow lenses, giving a double yellow effect, and help to diminish the power of the red lens being illuminated. This would help to explain why Hodder accelerated before even reaching the AWS magnet for signal SN109. Furthermore, the AWS warning which was given at signal SN109 is exactly what he would expect to receive at a double yellow, and served to confirm his error.

There is another theory, which concerns the visibility of the signals on Gantry 8. When this gantry initially comes into view, the red aspects of all six signals can be seen, *except SN109.* It is suggested that the inability to see the red aspect at SN109 at that point, because it is obstructed by an electrical insulator in the overhead wires, led Driver Hodder to the conclusion that the signal was other than at red. The warning at the AWS magnet would be irrelevant.

It is interesting to see that fibre-optic searchlight signals are being introduced in the Paddington area. This new design of signal is lighter than the standard signal head and requires much less maintenance because the light source is away from the signal head. A lighter structure can therefore be used to support the signal head, which can be mounted lower down on signal gantries, improving the driver's sighting of the signal. Searchlight signals have only one lens, which is uncoloured, and therefore they are not susceptible to a misleading phantom effect.

Whatever caused Driver Hodder to pass SN109 can only be speculated upon, but it emphasises the need to provide an improved AWS as quickly as possible. TPWS would have prevented the Ladbroke Grove collision. The driver might not have triggered the speed trap at 40mph but he would certainly have triggered the train stop at the signal. That would have stopped his train in a very short distance and within the overlap.

The actions of the signallers

In Slough New signalbox, known as an Integrated Electronic Control Centre (IECC), Signaller Allen was on duty at workstation No 1 at the time of the accident. That workstation controlled the line from Paddington to Acton East and included Ladbroke Grove. There were two other signallers in the Control Room at the time, at workstations 2 and 3 respectively. There was no supervisor's post.

Mr Allen had joined BR in 1981 and had 11 years' experience as a signaller before moving to the Slough IECC about 1995. He had been a signaller grade 10, the highest grade, for about five years. He was working his seventh successive 12-hour shift, ironically in order to cover other signallers who were attending the Southall Inquiry.

He heard an alarm sound, and looked at the alarm screen. It indicated that train 1K20 (the 'Thames Turbo') had passed signal SN109 at Danger. He said at the inquiry:

'. . . there was a short period of time when I was expecting the driver to come on the phone and say that he had passed the signal at Danger. It was only then when he progressed over the junction I knew that we not only had a SPAD but that we had a train running away . . .'. (The report explains that his use of the word 'junction' meant the stage when the train proceeded on to track circuit GF, the second track circuit beyond SN109.)

Mr Allen stated that he shouted that 1K20 (Hodder's train) had passed a signal at Danger and that Mr Hillman came over to help him. Hillman then sent an emergency Stop message to the driver of the 'Turbo' via the Cab Secure Radio system. Allen changed his VDU screen from overview to the detailed screen for Ladbroke Grove with a view to attempting to change Points 8059 and divert 1K20 to the down relief line, but he was too late. The evidence regarding the sending of the emergency Stop message is very garbled, but Lord Cullen was satisfied that it was sent. However, he states that, owing to the poor quality of the evidence, it is unsafe to determine whether it was received before the collision, let alone how long before it.

At this stage it would probably be helpful to give details of the various instructions to signallers in the event of a SPAD. Those listed in the report are as follows:

Regulation 47 of the Signalling General Instructions, dated August 1999, states:
'47.1. If a train passes a signal at danger without authority, the signaller must immediately arrange for the movement to be stopped by the most appropriate means and take any other emergency action.'
'47.2. The signaller must then make sure the Driver is advised of the circumstances, arranging for the driver to contact him immediately.'

The SPAD alarm, recommended by Lord Cullen to alert signallers immediately to the occurrence of a SPAD. These are being provided in IECCs and will give a distinctive audible alarm and a visual message, which will identify the signal and train concerned, if possible. *GWT*

Regulation 4.1.1 of the Track Circuit Block Regulations, dated August 1999, states:
'If it is necessary to stop trains because of any obstruction of the line or other emergency, the signaller must place or maintain the necessary signals at Danger to protect the line affected.'

Regulation 4.3 of the Track Circuit Block Regulations states:
'If the signaller is unable to stop a train proceeding into an affected section, he must comply with regulation 6.'

Regulation 6 of the Track Circuit Block Regulations states:
'6.1. If the signaller becomes aware . . . that a train is proceeding without authority . . . he must:
a) place or maintain at Danger the signals for any line which may be affected in order to stop any other train which may be endangered;
b) place or maintain the signals at Danger against the . . . runaway train except as shown below;
c) take all practicable steps to avoid a collision, such as . . . diverting the runaway train to another line which is clear.'

Section 1 of the 'Instructions to Signallers at Slough New' where it deals with 'Driver-Only Operation of Passenger Trains (DOO{P}) "Cab Secure Radio" System', states:
'Should you require to stop a DOO(P) train in emergency you must immediately carry out the procedure for sending a STOP message. This is in addition to the placing/maintaining of signals at Danger, and the carrying out of any local instructions.'

It is commendable that Lord Cullen managed to make sense of all these instructions, but no doubt his legal training

A signaller's workstation in Upminster Integrated Electronic Control Centre (IECC).
Author's collection

allowed him to do so. The regulations carry with them a great deal of railway history and in essence have changed little over the years. They are designed for the traditional railway, controlled by lineside signals, which were the signaller's only means of communicating with the driver. In such a world all the signaller can do is to put signals to danger and divert the runaway train if possible. Those are the two essentials and should be done the instant a SPAD becomes known. However, on the modern railway, radio communication is available and it is clear, as one of the witnesses observes, that:

'. . . the traditional way of trying to deal with an emergency has been to try and put signals back to Danger, and that seems to have been carried on even though other methods such as Cab Secure Radio have become available and may be more appropriate. I do not really think that that has sunk into the culture of signallers as to how they should deal with emergency situations.'

This witness was Mr W. G. Boddy, a very experienced signal engineer who was a past president of the Institution of Railway Signal Engineers.

Lord Cullen was more scathing in his criticism:

'The general picture which emerged was of a slack and complacent regime, which was not alive to the potentially dire consequences of a SPAD or of the way in which signallers could take action to deal with such situations.'

Note that he was referring to signallers of the highest grade with many years' experience. The inherited culture did not emphasise the value of Cab Secure Radio. They were waiting to see if 1K20 stopped 'because that was the normal practice'. It has to be admitted that the drivers of trains which have passed a signal at Danger almost always recognise that they have done so and bring their trains to a stand, usually within the overlap. But 1K20 was the exception, and by 'waiting to see' the signallers lost precious seconds in which a radio Stop message to 1K20 might have enabled the driver to stop his train before he reached the conflicting point with the HST, or at least to reduce the speed of the collision.

The report examines this particular point in great detail. It calculates that there was a period of 18 seconds after 1K20 passed SN109 signal in which an emergency application of the brakes would have stopped the train clear of the HST. Part of that 18 seconds would have been taken up by receipt of the alarm, the sending of the Stop message by radio, by the driver reacting, and by the operation of the brake, which together could have occupied up to 10 seconds. It is necessary to stress that that is based on a number of estimates, but if it is correct, there were eight seconds available for the Stop message to be acted upon. That is a very short time, and it raises an interesting question of how quickly a signaller, fully relaxed and not necessarily looking at his VDU screens or the section of line concerned, can switch himself to a state of high alertness and get the adrenaline flowing.

One of the witnesses, Dr Lucas, said concerning this issue:

'When the time comes for a person controlling an automatic system to intervene, it takes them some time to get a mental picture of what actually is going on, because that is harder to do . . . than when you are actually physically controlling it.'

The vital instruction following a SPAD is contained in the Instructions to Signallers at Slough New — '. . . you must immediately carry out the procedure for sending a Stop message' — but it is clear that the various instructions to signallers on this vital issue need rationalising so that they appear in only one place and not in four.

Lord Cullen recommended that there should be a unique alarm for SPADs in Integrated Electronic Control Centres (IECCs), and these are now being provided. They give an audible alarm and a visual message, identifying as far as possible the train and signal involved. A typical visual message would read 'SPAD by [train number] 1A23 at [signal N] S456', thus alerting the signaller immediately.

The involvement of HM Railway Inspectorate

There is a popular, but quite false, impression that HMRI keeps a close watch on everything that the railway industry does. To do this it would require a huge army of inspectors, and those inspectors would have to be highly qualified and technically proficient, with considerable experience in the fields of railway engineering and operations in all their many aspects. They would, in effect, have to second-guess everything that the industry did.

On 23 June 1999 a Class 142 'Pacer' unit ran past a signal at danger at the end of the down slow line near Winsford where it converges with the down fast line. The unit stopped on the down fast line about 400yd north of the junction and was run into by a Virgin express, the 06.30 from Euston to Glasgow. There were no trap points at the end of the down slow line. *Alan Sherratt*

Even if it were desirable to have such an army of experts, it could never be achieved. In the first place, such a pool of experts does not exist outside railway circles and to poach them from the railway industry would create such a vacuum that it would be impossible to run the railway, let alone to do so safely. Secondly, in order to attract recruits in sufficient numbers from either the railway industry or from the many consultancies and private firms that have sprung up in the wake of privatisation, it would be necessary to pay much higher salaries than are presently in operation. The Civil Service could not allow this because it would cost too much and would distort pay scale relativities within the Civil Service. And, finally, most railwaymen and engineers want to be in the front line and run the railway, rather than watch others doing it. A huge HMRI would not provide the necessary degree of job satisfaction for most people.

It is, therefore, instructive to examine the staffing levels and shortages in HMRI during the period of the Paddington modernisation, between 1993 and 1999. Alan Cooksey, the Deputy Chief Inspector of Railways, gave evidence that:

'HMRI had about six inspectors, roughly half of what the complement should have been. A lot of New Work Schemes were coming through. We were simply overwhelmed with work. We had gone from something like 350-400 active schemes to something in the order of 1,300 . . . The Jubilee Line was an enormous drain on our resources. We were dealing with the Channel Tunnel rail link and the West Coast Main Line project. We had something like 20-odd different train builds in progress.'

Lord Cullen comments that management should surely have pressed for increased resources. This assumes that they would have been forthcoming. What happened was that HSE transferred personnel from other branches of the HSE, most of whom had little or no experience of railways, whilst some of the existing inspectors who were both experienced and technically qualified became disgruntled and left the

Inspectorate, often to work in companies that support the railway industry. On any rational assessment, this must be regarded as highly unsatisfactory.

However, it is time to relate the story of HMRI's involvement in the Paddington modernisation scheme, bearing in mind the shortage of inspectors. On 26 February and 22 April 1993 HMRI granted InterCity Great Western provisional approval of Phase 1 of the scheme for resignalling from Paddington to Kensal Green, subject to the works being inspected in due course. There was no objection to the works being brought into use before such inspection, subject to there being compliance with any requirements of the inspecting officer. This was standard practice and had applied for many years.

In the meantime, the HSE altered the system of approvals. Provisional approval ceased to be available, but the new Regulations, known as 'The Railways and Other Transport Systems (Approval of Works, Plant and Equipment) Regulations 1994, allowed new or altered works to be used before approval where to do otherwise would cause serious disruption to existing services (Reg 4 [4][a]). This allowed the Paddington resignalling to be used for an extended period until sufficient information was available for HMRI to consider an application for approval. As will become clear, this position was never reached because the scheme never reached finality. Once again, HSE had discarded a tried and tested system and replaced it with something less practical and certainly less effective. There was no reason for the change.

HMRI inspected Phase 1 early in 1995 and Mr Cooksey wrote to the Zone Director warning him that there were some questionable issues which might result in full approval not being possible. There were 27 such issues, including, significantly: 'There are a number of instances where the signals are considered to be poorly positioned from a driver's sighting point of view . . .'.

He also stated that the level of SPADs gave rise to concern regarding signal sighting problems which were likely to be made worse by the erection of OHLE structures. Thus formal approval could not be given.

On 17 May 1996, over a year later, the Project Manager advised HMRI of the current position in regard to the outstanding issues. He said that a detailed signal sighting exercise had been completed and the effect of the OHLE equipment had resulted in a negligible effect to signalling. However, it is alleged that the exercise consisted merely of someone looking at the signals whilst walking along the line. This was quite different from a Signal Sighting Committee carrying out a proper examination. If the allegation is correct it supports a view that judicial inquiries do not always reveal the whole truth.

Phase 2 of the scheme was inspected by HMRI in October and November 1996, and again there were a number of issues which required action. On 27 March 1997, Railtrack sent to HMRI a list of actions and timetables to enable approval of Phases 1 and 2 of the resignalling scheme to be granted. These were still in hand when the Southall accident occurred on 19 September 1997. HMRI took the view that it would be inappropriate to approve the signalling scheme until the inquiry into the accident at Southall had been concluded and any concerns which had been expressed about signalling had been taken into account. This was proved to have been an unwise decision. The Southall Inquiry was greatly delayed whilst the BT Police laboriously prepared its case for criminal prosecution, and in the event the resignalling scheme was not approved before the collision at Ladbroke Grove.

The HSE attempted to shift the blame on to its own HMRI for not pursuing the issues more vigorously and for putting too much trust in Railtrack, but the inquiry revealed the HSE's own shortcomings in not providing the necessary resources of the required quality. So far as trust is concerned, this chapter has demonstrated the all-pervasive and enduring nature of the railway culture. Before the former Railway Inspectorate was absorbed into the HSE in 1990 there had been a bond of trust between the Inspectorate and BR which had existed for many years and which the HSE described as 'a light touch form of regulation'. That trust no longer existed, but it was not immediately apparent, and inspectors in the field tended still to trust Railtrack. The HSE said that HMRI was now less willing to accept, when Railtrack said that something would be done, that it would be done and that it would be done in the timescale that was promised.

Lord Cullen decided that he would deal with the question of HMRI's functions in Part 2 of his inquiry, and this important question will be examined in Chapter 8.

The crashworthiness of the coaches

It was generally felt that the Mk 3 coaches of the HSTs had demonstrated once again their remarkable capacity for maintaining the structural integrity of the coach bodies, a very considerable tribute to British Rail Engineering. The only criticism of substance was the tendency of the bogies

to become detached and cause damage. However, it has to be remembered that a coach body bereft of its bogies may cause far less damage to other vehicles than if its bogies were intact. It was also noticed that the bogie-retaining straps fitted to vehicles may in certain circumstances contribute to derailments through inhibiting the necessary freedom of the coach body and the bogie to move away from each other on rough track. The wisdom or otherwise of bogie-retaining straps is still a matter of debate.

The very severe damage and high number of deaths in the 'Thames Turbo' appears to have been accepted by experts as the inevitable consequence of a head-on collision at 130mph, but a number of fairly modest recommendations were made for improvement. Much consideration was given to the suitability of aluminium welding for the construction of coach bodies, but expert evidence was given at the inquiry that the extent of casualties would have been as great even if the bodies had been made of steel. There is increasing interest in a new process known as 'friction stir welding', which has a potential to improve the crashworthiness of aluminium vehicles that could otherwise fail in the heat-affected zone along weld seams.

There was some concern at the manner in which tables in the HST gave way under the impact of passengers being propelled forward at 80mph when the crash occurred. Very serious internal injuries can be caused to passengers facing the direction of travel by impact with the edge of a table, and if it were less collapsible those injuries would be worsened. This has to be set against the injuries that may be sustained by a passenger seated opposite with back to the engine if struck by the edge of a detached table propelled forward by the weight of the passenger opposite. It is important to maintain a proper balance on this issue.

Fire

This is one of the weakest sections of the report. It is dealt with in less than two pages and this would seem to indicate Lord Cullen's ready acceptance of expert opinion that the fuel tanks of trains could not have been expected to withstand the extreme forces which were generated in the crash. A number of measures were proposed that are little more than a wish list, but include one which states that trains should carry less fuel. The effect of this on train utilisation is not assessed.

Is it beyond the wit of man to design a fuel tank which is sufficiently strong for its purpose, or is the inquiry saying in effect that it is not necessary to do anything other than cosmetic because ATP/TPWS/ERTMS will avoid collisions in future? The history of oil fuel fires on Great Western HSTs, listed below, gives no comfort for such complacency.

But all is not lost. The journal *Railnews* reports that the Health & Safety laboratory has been testing a series of designs that could improve the crashworthiness of fuel tanks by putting specially designed structures inside them. A number of TOCs and manufacturers are involved in the project, which is being funded by the HSE and the rail companies.

On 16 February 1979 a crowded HST from Paddington was travelling at about 65mph just beyond Reading when it ran into two lengths of rail which had been placed across the down main line by vandals in such a manner that one of them was angled upwards towards the approaching train.

The upturned rail split the fuel tank of the leading power car and fire broke out instantly, enveloping the first three coaches in flames before the train could be stopped. However, the fire did not penetrate the coaches and rapidly died out.

On 8 September 1995 a serious fire occurred on a crowded HST from Paddington as it approached Maidenhead when one of the diesel fuel tanks became partially detached and ruptured as it impacted against the track. The spilt fuel ignited and enveloped the front part of the train. Fumes penetrated a part of the train through the toilet-waste fallpipe and one man was killed when he jumped out of the train into the path of another train.

Evacuation of the train

The need for passengers to leave a train urgently following an accident is extremely rare, and in most cases it is preferable for passengers to stay in the train until they are rescued. Jumping out in an uncontrolled fashion exposes them to risks from passing trains or from electrocution. None the less, Lord Cullen devotes no fewer than 22 pages and almost a third of his recommendations to this issue, which, despite the awful circumstances at Ladbroke Grove, might be considered excessive bearing in mind that the last time a passen-

ger was killed in fire following a collision was over 70 years ago.

There is an obvious danger in allowing pressure groups to have a platform at railway accident inquiries. It is a very recent development and is quite undesirable. Whilst one has the greatest sympathy with the injured and bereaved, it is inevitable that their judgements are coloured by their awful experiences. This is hardly a good basis for objective and dispassionate study and assessment of the issues arising. In any event, it is unlikely that survivors themselves have the necessary technical knowledge or experience to make a judgement, and they have to rely on expert opinion. Even then, there is an inevitable human tendency to accept only that expert opinion which supports one's views, and to refuse to accept other expert views. In the Ladbroke Grove case the villain of the piece was seen to be Railtrack, despite the fact that the driver was not its employee nor was it responsible for crashworthiness and the fire.

How good was the report?

Much of the report is good and to the point, but it has some weaknesses too. He commends risk analysis but he has not applied it in his recommendations as frequently and as thoroughly as necessary, leaving a feeling that he is looking for perfection, rather than taking a practical and realistic approach. Has he forgotten that old lawyer's maxim that hard cases make bad law? One would have appreciated a greater understanding of the situation facing the signallers when the SPAD alarm sounded, and a more thorough examination of driver training. The chapters on fire and crashworthiness are weak, whereas far too much space is given to evacuation of trains. However, those criticisms apart, many sections of the report are excellent, and reveal Lord Cullen at his best.

The front coaches of the First Great Western High Speed Train (HST) lie on their sides following the collision at Ladbroke Grove on 4 October 1999. Note how well the coach bodies have survived the impact — a tribute to the 25-year-old design of the Mk 3 coaches. They are commonly regarded as being some of the best rolling stock ever built, both before and since. *Modern Railways*

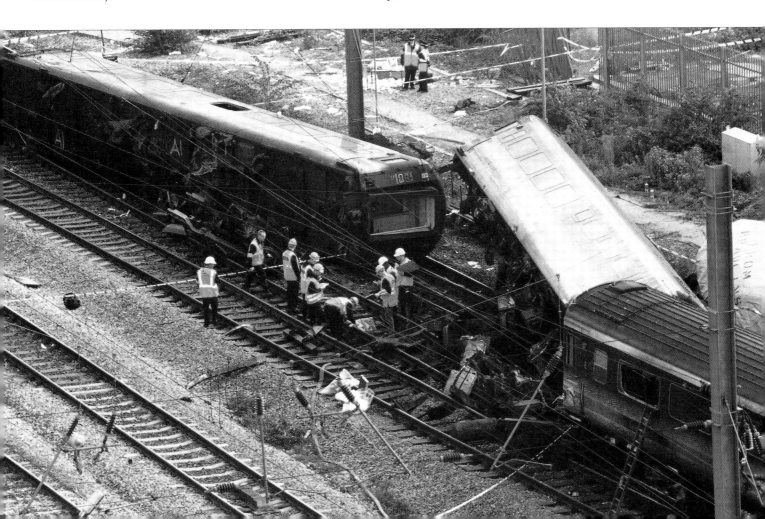

7 Train protection systems — the David Davies Report

Terms of reference

Following the collision at Ladbroke Grove, on 9 October 1999 the Deputy Prime Minister, John Prescott, asked Sir David Davies CBE, FREng, FRS, President of the Royal Academy of Engineering, to undertake an independent review of possible forms of Automatic Train Protection (ATP) suitable for fitting on the national rail network and associated rolling stock in order to achieve improvements in railway safety and protection from signals passed at danger (SPADs).

Train protection is a rather strange term. It prompts the question: 'Protection against what?' The term 'protection' is of very ancient lineage. It was originally applied to the prevention of a collision with a disabled or derailed train (known as Protection of the Train) or any other form of obstruction (Protection of the Line). It was intended to give prompt protection against a train running into danger, which could not be given by the signalling system. It had nothing

to do with signals being passed at danger. The modern use of the term concerns the safety of a train, and any other train which may be involved, when a train passes a signal at danger, or travels too fast.

John Prescott initiated this review because he was under considerable pressure from the media, and particularly from survivors and bereaved groups, who called vociferously for ATP immediately, at any price. He recognised that railway industry sources would not be seen in the public eye to be giving independent advice; the obvious source, Railtrack, was low in public esteem at that time. The railway industry knew that the Train Protection & Warning System (TPWS) was the preferred choice over ATP because it could be implemented much sooner than ATP and at a much lower cost. ATP of the prescribed standard type, known as the European Train Control System (ETCS), was still in the development stage and no firm date could be given as to when it would be available for use.

The Deputy Prime Minister might have adopted the alternative course of asking the government safety regulator, the Health & Safety Commission, to advise on the options, using HM Railway Inspectorate. That would have been the normal course, because advice to ministers had traditionally been one of the responsibilities of the Railway Inspectorate, but neither the HSC nor HMRI were highly regarded at the time by John Prescott (or indeed by the media), and he clearly felt that recommendations from such a source would carry insufficient weight.

Freight trains now run at high speed with heavy loads, pointing the need for effective protection against signals accidentally being passed at Danger. EWS Class 60 diesel-electric locomotive No 60005 is seen passing Cardiff Canton EWS Traction Depot on 4 May 2001, at the head of the 05.23 from Wolverhampton to Margam. The train will return loaded with steel. *Brian Morrison*

Hence he appointed an independent engineer to investigate and report on the issue, with the following terms of reference:

- To assess the different available systems of train protection that could be used on the heavy rail network and advise, in particular, on their effectiveness, practicability and cost.

- To assess the rail industry's response to the increase in the number of signals passed at danger on the national rail network, which was highlighted in the HSE's report of 2 September 1999, including the industry's actions to implement that report's findings; and to advise on further ways of reducing the number of signals passed at danger.

- To report back to the Deputy Prime Minister by the end of December 1999, with initial advice if the full assessments are not complete by then.

- This report, and any subsequent reports, are to be published and made available to Professor John Uff so that he can take account of them in the recommendations arising from his public inquiry into the Southall rail crash.

The scene near Wembley station on the West Coast main line on 11 October 1984, after the 17.54 electric multiple-unit from Euston to Bletchley had passed a signal at danger and collided at a converging point with a Freightliner train which was just leaving Willesden Sidings. Three passengers were killed and a number injured. It was a clear warning that AWS was not foolproof. *Mick Roberts*

Sir David Davies was assisted by Dr Alan Cribbens, formerly of the BR Research Department, and Mr Roger Taylor, of Railtrack's Safety & Standards Directorate. His report was published with remarkable promptitude in February 2000.

What is the price of a life?

One of the popular issues of the day was related to the practical question of the value to be placed on a human life, particularly when assessing potential capital expenditure. The 'ATP at any price' faction did not accept any limits on expenditure so long as passenger train crashes with loss of life could be avoided in the future. They had a burning desire to avoid a repetition of Ladbroke Grove whatever the cost, and they considered cost to be an irrelevance.

Sir David Davies stated that, in reality, there was no way of putting a cost on human life, but when considering means of accident prevention the use of economic criteria was important in the consideration of alternative safety investments. So far as road traffic was concerned, he mentioned a figure of £0.75 million per fatality prevented as a guideline used by the Department of Transport when considering investment in road schemes. This is much lower than guideline figures for rail investment, a figure of £2.7 million being quoted, although he admits that there are many examples of much higher figures. There is no logic in this difference, except that road accidents are commonplace whereas rail accidents are rare, less than one a year in which passengers are killed. There is a common perception that the passenger relies upon the railway company to get him to his destination unharmed, whereas a car driver is responsible for his own destiny. The latter view is not wholly true. Car, bus and coach passengers put their lives in the driver's hands, and in fatal crashes innocent people are often killed, including drivers.

The need for train protection

The report accepts the need for some improved form of train protection, with a choice of two systems. It quotes a study by consultants W. S. Atkins which concluded that TPWS would have prevented 2.8 equivalent fatalities a year on average, compared with 4.3 for an ideal ATP system, representing an overall effectiveness of 65%. (The term 'equivalent fatalities' includes a slight weighting to provide for injuries.) The cost of installing TPWS was estimated to be £335 million for track equipment and £50 million for on-train equipment, a total of £385 million. Over a 20-year period 56 equivalent fatalities would be avoided, giving a figure of approximately £7 million per equivalent fatality. There are two problems with such forecasts. Costs seem to rise inexorably above the original estimates, and the number of casualties is abnormally influenced by a major disaster every 10 years or so. However, taking history as a guide, between 1980 and 2000 119 passengers lost their lives in train accidents. Drivers were predominantly responsible for 54 of those fatalities. Subsequent safeguards would have avoided 12 of those 54, and the remaining 42 all had the potential of being avoided by TPWS. This seems to confirm the figure quoted above of 2.8 equivalent fatalities a year.

ATP was estimated to cost £730 million for track costs and about £423 million for rolling stock. Railtrack stated that based on past experience it would be advisable to add a significant margin of say 50% to allow for risks and many unforeseen issues, giving a total estimated costs for ATP of £1,729,000,000, about £1.7 billion. W. S. Atkins' study indicated a potential saving of 4.3 equivalent lives a year, equal to 86 over a 20-year-period, at a cost of almost exactly £20 million per equivalent life. That is without TPWS. If TPWS were to be installed, the potential saving achieved by installing ATP in addition would be 1.5 equivalent lives a year, at a cost approaching £60 million per equivalent life saved.

However, the railway industry is under an obligation to install TPWS. It is a requirement under the Railway Safety Regulations 1999, issued by the HSE, and provides that a suitable system must be installed by the end of 2003. The regulations require all passenger railways, and all trains which operate on them, to be fitted with a train protection system which will automatically apply the brakes if the train passes a stop signal without authorisation, or if a train approaches a stop signal or a speed restriction at excessive speed. The train protection system is to be provided at all signals which protect converging or opposing train movements, also on the approach to all buffer stops and on the approach to severe permanent or temporary speed restrictions. The regulations do not specifically mention TPWS, but programmes for the installation of TPWS by Railtrack and Train Operating Companies have been approved by HMRI as conforming to the regulations. So, in effect, the decision on a suitable form of train protection has already been made. But John Prescott needed some way to pacify the media and the survivors and bereaved groups, and to buy time for the pressures to abate, hence the study by Sir David Davies.

On any rational assessment, the cost of ATP cannot be justified, even without TPWS, but there are other influences. Issues of investment of such magnitude cannot be considered in isolation, even in respect of a privatised railway. The present railway industry relies heavily on public funds, and investment in ATP would have to be funded either by the public purse or through higher fares. Would either course be politically acceptable? Supporters of ATP at any price would have suggested that shareholders' dividends should be reduced to pay for ATP, but without sufficient dividends Railtrack would have been unable to attract investment from the City. The position has, of course, changed since this report was published, by the creation of Network Rail, a company limited by guarantee, to replace Railtrack. There are now no dividends, and surplus funds, if any, will be reinvested.

The future vision for train protection

In some ways the future of train protection in Britain, and indeed the whole of Europe, has already been settled. In the early 1990s the European Commission began to consider the use of directives which would apply across the European Community to harmonise the operation of railway systems in interconnected member states and facilitate through working. In particular, signalling and safety systems have developed almost independently in the different European countries, including Britain.

In 1996, the European Council adopted the High Speed Train Interoperability Directive (96/48/EC), providing for interoperability of the high-speed Trans-European Network, generally known as the TEN lines. This directive was adopted in Britain on 16 May 2002 under the terms of the Railways (High-Speed) (Interoperability) Regulations 2002. In Britain, the TEN lines include:

- The Great Western main line
- The West Coast main line
- The East Coast main line
- The Channel Tunnel rail link

The first three lines will be upgraded for speeds of 125mph and above, and *when upgraded*, will require to be equipped with a train protection system. The essential requirements are to be met by the adoption of 'Technical Specifications for Interoperability' (TSIs). A European committee has been working on the production of the TSIs, including one covering the control-command and signalling sub-system.

The train protection systems which have to be fitted under the Interoperability Directive will come within the European Rail Traffic Management System (ERTMS).

In addition, the European Commission has published a directive on the interoperability of conventional lines, broadly in line with the High Speed Directive. The two directives will cover most of Britain's rail network.

Sir David Davies believes that the future vision for train control and train protection for the national network must lie with the European Train Control System (ETCS, part of ERTMS), and ultimately with the advanced Level 3, described in the following chapters. He regards the most important aspects of Level 3 as its ability to provide increased line capacity and faster recovery from delays in a disrupted traffic pattern, but he recognises that it will not be available for some years. The ultimate aim must be a control system which is operated through radio channels and where there is the minimum of lineside equipment, ie no lineside signals and no track-based train detection systems. The instructions currently given to the driver by the lineside signals, which have the potential for misunderstanding, will be given to him on the console in his driving cab.

The need for immediate action

The Ladbroke Grove accident emphasised the need for a safer system of train protection to be installed and brought into use as soon as possible. ETCS would provide a higher standard of safety than the TPWS currently being installed, but in order to achieve early benefits the TPWS programme must be allowed to continue, and be accelerated if possible. If the TPWS programme were to be stopped (as at December 1999) in favour of ETCS, passengers would be no better protected for many years than they were at Ladbroke Grove.

The new and not so new thread their way through the tangle of lines outside Manchester Piccadilly on 17 September 2001. Centre left is a late-1980s vintage Class 158 DMU; on the right is a new Class 175 'Coradia' DMU operated by First North Western. It forms the 11.49 from Manchester Airport to Barrow-in-Furness. *Brian Morrison*

There would have to be trials and there would be substantial delay in designing and fitting a safety system and proving that it was fully safe and durable. There would be the complexity of equipping older rolling stock. Nationwide fitting would take many years, whereas TPWS will certainly be installed system-wide by the end of 2003, and earlier at many places.

The report acknowledges the admitted disadvantages of TPWS, which it lists as:

- The system is not inherently fail-safe.

- The effectiveness of the speed trap to stop a train within the overlap of the signal is limited to a maximum speed of 75mph. (But the critical factor is to stop a train before it reaches a conflict point, which may be some distance beyond the end of the overlap.)

- It assumes an emergency braking rate of 12%g, but not all stock will be able to achieve this by 2003.

However, the effectiveness of TPWS is not in principle limited in performance to 75mph and the report notes that work is in progress on an enhanced version of TPWS, known as TPWS+, able to operate at speeds up to 100mph by the use of an additional speed trap further away from the signal at about 800m. The additional cost is estimated to be about £70 million. TPWS+ has been on trial at several sites in the

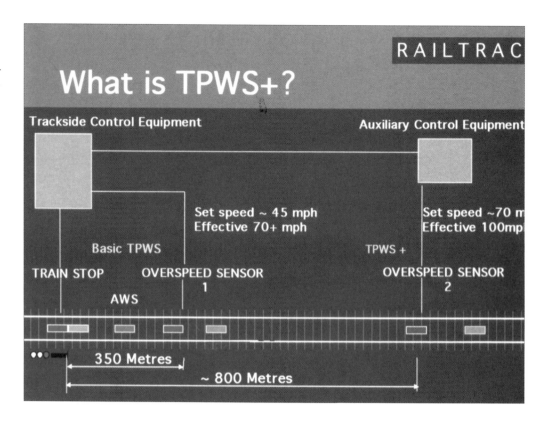

Doncaster and Hitchin areas since June 2001, and Network Rail intends to fit it at those locations where it will offer most benefit, principally approaching busy junctions.

Summary of the report's recommendations for fitment of train protection

1. Take forward the current accelerated plan for fitting standard TPWS, completing track work by the end of 2002 and train fitment by 2003.
2. Take forward other plans in the 1999 Rail Safety Summit, such as improved driver training and defensive driving practices.
3. Establish an urgent trials programme for TPWS+, leading to a decision to adopt it.
4. Fit enhancement to TPWS during 2003.
5. Examine the option of extended coverage of existing ATP on the Great Western main line. Examine the possible value of any extension of the Chiltern ATP installation.
6. Take forward the current ETCS programme on the West Coast main line from 2002.
7. Fit ETCS on the East Coast main line based on the experience of the West Coast main line. Bring forward the start date to 2006 if possible.
8. Upgrade and convert Great Western main line ATP to ETCS when appropriate.
9. Extend full ATP to other lines running above 100mph (eg Midland main line).
10. Establish a UK pilot for ETCS Level 3, in approximately 2008.
11. New stock is to be designed to accommodate ETCS equipment.

12. A recommendation re defensive driving and the fitting of data recorders.
13. The programme of fitting enhanced emergency braking to be continued as fast as possible.

Comments on the recommendations

The report is strongly in favour of continuing to install TPWS with all speed, and to take advantage of enhancements, such as TPWS+ for trains above 75mph, and emergency enhanced braking. It reasonably suggests extending BR-ATP on parts of the Great Western main line and the Chiltern line. Whilst recommending ETCS, the report is on less sure ground in proposing dates, at a time when the Technical Specifications had not been finalised and ETCS systems were a long way from being available. Such dates have little basis in reality (and subsequently have been shown to be over-optimistic) but no doubt the author of the report felt he had to make some sort of estimate, lest he be accused of being too vague.

So far as the Deputy Prime Minister was concerned, the report gave him support for continuing with TPWS, and adopting ETCS in due course. There was no other sensible alternative. It was important to have the increased protection of TPWS as quickly as possible, but it also entailed increased expenditure overall, some of which might have a short life if ETCS came to be implemented fairly quickly. However, given a long experience of implementing complex technical systems such as ETCS, it was undoubtedly the correct decision. ETCS is mandatory by virtue of the European Commission's directives, and will have to be adopted (although there is a derogation facility), but it could take several, indeed, many years before its installation is widespread. To have abandoned TPWS (which would have had to be by ministerial direction — he would have had to rescind the 1999 Railway

Another photograph, taken on 25 October 2001, depicting the old and the new. Within the lofty portals of the impressive Glasgow Central station stand, on the right, a 1980s-vintage Class 156 'Super Sprinter', now past its half-life, and on the left a shiny new Class 334 'Juniper' electric multiple-unit. The Class 334s are excellent trains, but like many other new builds they have had protracted teething troubles. Here, unit No 334026 forms the 12.40 Cathcart Circle train. *Brian Morrison*

Regulations which mandated TPWS) would have condemned passengers for many years to a level of safety no higher than that which applied before Ladbroke Grove. That would have been unthinkable and irresponsible, but there were siren voices pressing for ATP now and the abandonment of TPWS. They had been misled, and it is fortunately that they were not heeded. Had they been, passengers' lives would have been sacrificed unnecessarily. It was an episode that illustrated the danger of allowing untrained and ill-informed groups, no matter how well-meaning, to have a platform. The TPWS/ATP debate is discussed more thoroughly in succeeding chapters.

Conclusions

The report rightly points out that nothing is completely safe, and it is a nonsense to suggest that the railways can ever be free from accidents. In the 20 years 1980–2000, fewer than half of all passenger fatalities in train accidents resulted from drivers passing signals at danger. The remainder were from diverse causes. Indeed, none of the three serious accidents since Ladbroke Grove, discussed in the following chapters, was caused by a driver's error.

The 1999 Railway Regulations mandated the provision of TPWS on approaches to buffer stops. This was an absurd decision which wasted a lot of money and diverted scarce technical resources from more productive tasks. Since 1964 there have been two passenger fatalities caused by drivers crashing into buffer stops, and it is quite clear that the HSE, in mandating TPWS approaching buffer stops, had not carried out any quantified risk analysis nor considered the cost-effectiveness of the requirement. It demonstrated that the HSE was obsessed with rail safety at all costs, which was not the balanced judgement that one has a right to expect from such a body. It is the sort of action that brings the HSE into disrepute.

However, one should not dismiss the question of the urgent provision of ATP too lightly. Train speeds are continuing to increase above the capability of TPWS, and there are more trains on the line, leading potentially to more red signals. There is also the philosophical point that drivers deserve something better than TPWS. They have been neglected over the years, and it is an anachronism that they should have to peer out of the cab window in all weathers to locate a vital signal which is no more than a coloured light somewhere in the distance. Experience with BR-ATP demonstrates that drivers drive with more confidence with the assurance of ATP.

Finally, this was not to be the only report which appeared at the time on train protection systems in Britain, even though it seemed to say all that needed to be said, made sensible and practical recommendation in limited numbers (only 16!), and did so authoritatively. It should have sufficed, but Professor Uff and Lord Cullen obviously thought otherwise, as the next chapter will show.

⑧ The joint inquiry into train protection systems

The genesis of the joint inquiry

The issues which the joint inquiry was formed to deal with were originally included within the terms of reference of the Southall rail accident inquiry, chaired by Professor Uff QC (see Chapters 3 and 4). For reasons previously discussed, the inquiry hearings did not commence until 20 September 1999, over two years after the accident. Within two weeks the Ladbroke Grove accident happened. Lord Cullen was appointed the chairman of that public inquiry and was given wide terms of reference which included the issues of train protection.

To avoid duplication it was decided that the issue of train protection should be dealt with by a joint public inquiry, chaired jointly by Professor Uff and Lord Cullen, taking account of both the Southall and Ladbroke Grove accidents and the report of Sir David Davies (see previous chapter). This was agreed to by the Chairman of the Health & Safety Commission, William Callaghan, with the consent of the Deputy Prime Minister, John Prescott, by letter dated 5 November 1999. The two Chairmen were assisted by a technical assessor, Major A. G. B. King OBE, BSc, a former Inspecting Officer of the Railway Inspectorate who had considerable experience in, and knowledge of, railway safety issues. There is no indication of the extent to which they accepted his advice.

It is inevitable that the Uff/Cullen Inquiry would cover much of the same ground as the Sir David Davies report discussed in the previous chapter and there may be some repetition in this chapter. The fundamental difference is that the Uff/Cullen Inquiry was conducted in public, whilst Sir David Davies conducted his work in private.

List of train protection systems

Before proceeding further, it would no doubt be helpful to list the various train protection systems, which will be referred to by their initials:

ATC   The Great Western Railway's Automatic Train Control system

AWS   British Railways' Automatic Warning System

BR-ATP British Railways' Automatic Train Protection system

TPWS   The standard Train Protection & Warning System (also referred to as TPWS-A)

Train Protection & Warning System

TPWS is designed to prevent the 'Ding-ding and away' type of accident, in which a train starts away from a station stop and wrongly passes the platform starting signal at Danger. This has been a not infrequent occurrence, but the TPWS 'train stop' equipment at such signals will bring a train to an immediate stop should it pass a signal in those circumstances. The photographs show (*left*) a collision near Glasgow Bellgrove station on 6 March 1989 when two Class 303 units met head-on, killing a driver and a passenger, (*above*) a Class 303 unit standing in Bellgrove station, and (*right*) the platform starting signal cleared for the left-hand route at the junction. *Tom Noble (left) and author (above and right)*

TPWS+	TPWS adapted for speeds 75-100mph
TPWS-E	TPWS-A or TPWS+ using equipment compatible with ETCS
ERTMS	The European Rail Traffic Management System
ETCS	The European Train Control System (almost synonymous with ERTMS) — Levels 1, 2 and 3
GSM-R	Global System for Mobile Communication — Railways

The terms of reference of the inquiry

The Joint Inquiry was required to consider the following:

1. Train Protection and Warning Systems;

2. Future application of Automatic Train Protection Systems;

3. SPAD prevention measures;

taking account in particular of:

- the Southall accident on 19 September 1997;

- the rail accident at Ladbroke Grove Junction on 5 October 1999;

- the technical assessment for the Deputy Prime Minister of Rail Safety Systems by Sir David Davies;

with a view to making general recommendations with regard thereto.

The mode of the inquiry

The Joint Inquiry might be considered to duplicate the work of Sir David Davies, but there was a great deal of public interest in the question, and pressure from a number of parties who were represented at the Southall and Ladbroke Grove inquiries for the debate to be conducted in public.

Accordingly, the inquiry was held under the provisions of Sec 14(2)(b) of the Health & Safety at Work Act 1974, in the same manner as the inquiries into the Southall and Ladbroke Grove accidents. Proceedings were led by the inquiry counsel, Ian Burnett QC, and the following parties were represented:

- Amey Rail;
- Angel Train Contracts;
- Association of Train Operating Companies (ATOC);
- English, Welsh & Scottish Railway (the freight company);
- Health & Safety Executive;
- Passengers' Group, incorporating both the Ladbroke Grove and Southall Passengers group of solicitors;
- Railtrack;
- Rail Users' Committees;
- Shadow Strategic Rail Authority;
- The rail trade unions ASLEF and RMT.

No fewer than 55 witnesses were called to be examined in chief by the inquiry counsel, and then cross-examined by any or all of the legal representatives of the various parties who wished to do so. In addition, a further 27 people gave

written evidence. It was a very long drawn out, but very thorough, examination of the subject. The inquiry ran from 18 September to 13 October 2000 and its report was published on 29 March 2001.

List of questions to be addressed in the report

The principal questions for consideration by the Joint Inquiry had been identified by the counsel to the inquiry as follows:

1. Should the current plan to install trackside and trainborne TPWS be continued, curtailed or aborted?

2. (a) Should TPWS+ be subject to trials?
(b) If the trials are successful should TPWS+ be installed anywhere on the network and if so where and in what circumstances?

3. (a) Should TPWS-E be subject to trials?
(b) If the trials are successful should TPWS-E be installed anywhere on the network and if so where and in what circumstances?

4. To what extent should ETCS be installed on the network, in what order and to what timetable?

5. What should be the future of BR-ATP on Great Western and Chiltern Trains and the Heathrow Express?

What is the justification for any changes?

The risk of fatalities from signals passed at Danger (SPADs) is, to put it bluntly, tiny. The report equates it to an average of two per year, based on the previous 20 years. However, public perception is different, because SPADs are seen to have the potential for catastrophic accidents. There have been only three catastrophic accidents with multiple fatalities in the past 40 years — Hither Green in 1967, Clapham in 1988 and Ladbroke Grove in 1999 — and only the latter was caused by a SPAD, so it might be argued that the risk of a catastrophic SPAD is itself tiny — one in 40 years. But it is the Doomsday scenario which causes concern. A catastrophic SPAD could happen tomorrow, and that is what becomes fixed in the public's mind, despite its rarity. The concern about SPADs has become an obsession, fostered unthinkingly by no less a figure than the Deputy Prime Minister of the day who, above all, should have been cautious about, and aware of the problems caused by, making rash pronouncements.

The report suggests that public reaction to catastrophic rail accidents is a matter that should be taken into account in the making of decisions about rail safety. This is surely a false argument. *Informed* public opinion, maybe, but public opinion formed by the sensationalist press and the countless hours of media coverage is not a good basis for making complex technical decisions about safety, as was so clearly demonstrated at the inquiry.

This obsession with rail safety is a comparatively recent phenomenon, and has resulted in badly skewed perceptions. It was not always so. The report bravely admits that, in the past, railway crashes, even very major ones, did not produce the level of public reaction which currently results from any rail accident involving casualties. What has caused the change? There are at least five causes:

1. The Health & Safety at Work Act 1974 was designed to improve what is set out in its title — health and safety at work, ie for the workers. But there was a clause, inserted for whatever reason, which included, in addition to workers, the protection of persons not at work against risks arising out of the activities of persons at work. There is no suggestion that this was designed to protect rail passengers. It does not protect bus or coach passengers or even pedestrians against those who are driving in employment, and it appears to have been sometime before the HSE realised that the clause could be used in connection with rail accidents involving passengers rather than just employees. The HSE has received considerable publicity by doing so.

2. Most of the recent serious accidents have occurred in the vicinity of London, or in the London commuter belt, eg Watford Junction (1996), Southall (1997), Ladbroke Grove (1999), Hatfield (2000) and Potters Bar (2002). Television crews and reporters descend *en masse* on the scene in a few minutes and fill our television screens and newspapers for weeks, endlessly speculating and trying to derive the maximum amount of emotion and pathos from the accident. The 'hate' campaign waged against Railtrack was particularly reprehensible, and enormously damaging to the railway industry. In years past the media behaved more responsibly and contented itself with the facts; it did not whip up public opinion against the railways.

3. The legal profession has entered the scene in large measure. Three public inquiries in as many years have provided lucrative employment for a large number of lawyers, and the pursuit of compensation claims yet more.

4. The involvement of the British Transport Police has been of a much higher profile than previously, with an apparent anxiety to find grounds for criminal prosecution (see Chapter 10).

5. The privatisation of the railways has created a situation in which there is no person or organisation to speak for the railway industry, and it does not command the respect that even British Rail had. The evident problems of the fragmentation of the railway industry have led to popular allegations of 'profits before safety' and increased the likelihood of media attacks upon the industry.

The report recognises that there are certain difficulties in seeking to take account of the public's attitude to safety. A major research project which reported in 2000 revealed surprisingly that there was little or no support for any differ-

The elderly dual-traction Class 73 locomotive owned by the EWS freight company passes Coulsden on 25 June 2001 with the 11.22 empty MBA wagons from Tonbridge to Hither Green.
Brian Morrison

ential in the 'value of a life' when applied to road and rail, and gave little support for a scale of safety expenditure that was greater on rail than on road. It certainly demolished any justification for spending billions of pounds on Automatic Train Protection to save two lives per year, when such expenditure on road safety might save hundreds.

The report recognises, to its credit, that the sums which can be devoted to safety issues are necessarily limited. The legal position is that safety on the railway system is governed by the underlying principle of what is reasonably practicable, in accordance with the Health & Safety at Work Act 1974. The meaning of the term 'reasonably practicable' was considered by the Court of Appeal in a 1949 case concerning the National Coal Board, when one of the Law Lords stated that:

'Reasonably practicable . . . seems to me to imply that a computation must be made by the owner in which the quantum of risk is placed on one scale and the sacrifice involved in the measures necessary for averting the risk (whether in money, time or trouble) is placed in the other; and if it be shown that there is a gross disproportion between them, the risk being insignificant in relation to the sacrifice, the person on whom the duty is laid discharges the onus on him of proving that compliance was not reasonably practicable.'

This would appear to settle the issue that cost is a factor in the equation and that the railway industry cannot be compelled by the HSE to spend unjustified sums of money on safety issues. Mr E. Brian Gibbens had much the same to say in his report of the public inquiry into the Hixon level crossing accident in 1968. Spending perhaps £3 billion to save 40 lives over the next 20 years equates to £75 million per life, which is surely disproportionate in the terms of the Court of Appeal ruling.

The European Community involvement

Sir David Davies, in his report discussed in the previous chapter, dealt with European Commission directives aimed at harmonising train command and control systems throughout Europe, including Britain, in order to facilitate what is now known as interoperability (ie the ability to run trains from one country to another, and through another country, without a change of traction). The Cullen/Uff joint report deals with it more extensively. It mentions that the European Rail Traffic Management System (ERTMS) was initiated by the European Commission as far back as 1989. That system covers a range of issues, but the main interest is train control through the European Train Control System (ETCS) which was set up in 1991. The aim of that project was to prepare Technical Specifications for Interoperability (TSIs) with which individual systems must comply.

To delve into history for a moment, railways in the modern sense were first developed in Britain and the influence of British engineers and British technology was considerable. The standard British gauge of 4ft 8½in was adopted throughout most of Europe, making interoperability a practical possibility. Unfortunately, as railways developed, the different European countries designed their own signalling and train control systems. Whilst Britain developed the Automatic Warning System (AWS), other European countries developed their own train protection systems. Not only that, but

they developed their own signalling systems too, and their own Rules and Regulations for the operation of trains. So far as Britain was concerned, the problem of the mix of systems came to a head with the planning of the Channel Tunnel, with the result that all Eurostar trains running through the Channel Tunnel have to be fitted with a variety of train protection and control systems to be able to run on the railways of Britain, France and Belgium. One might add that a common European language might ease interoperability too, but that apparently is a problem that is too difficult for the European Commission to solve.

The European Commission issued Directive No 96/48/EC, which applies to high-speed TEN lines (which are lines considered to constitute the Trans-European Network), and will require the fitment of a standard ETCS system, replacing the wide variety of systems currently in use in Europe. The directive does not specify a timetable for fitment, but requires ETCS to be installed *when renewal or upgrading of signalling* is taking place. This is an important caveat. A further European Directive, 2001/16/EC, is being issued on the interoperability of the trans-European conventional rail system. When it is implemented it will cover practically the whole European rail network, including Britain. But note a further caveat that the Strategic Rail Authority may apply for derogation if the fitment of ETCS may threaten the viability of a particular signalling project.

ETCS, in its higher levels, will make use of a new radio communications technology to create an entirely new command and control system for the railway. Communication will be via the Global System for Mobile Communication — Railways (GSM-R), similar to modern cell-phone technology.

The report describes the three levels of ETCS as follows:

- *Level 1* — this provides full Automatic Train Protection with continuous speed supervision and intermittent transmission from track to train, based on the track-mounted Eurobalise (a form of transponder) which is linked to a lineside electronic unit and conventional signals, and passes information to the train electronically. It is very similar in operation to the BR-ATP system in use on the Great Western line from Paddington and the Chilterns line from Marylebone. The operation of trains remains based on the conventional fixed block track circuit system. The signalling system is unchanged.
- *Level 2* — lineside signals are replaced by the very high integrity GSM-R radio network, which enables movement authorities to be transmitted direct to the train and displayed in the driving cab. Continuous speed supervision and continuous track-to-train communication is provided, but the operation of trains and information about their location is still based on fixed track blocks. Track-based train detection systems (ie track circuits or axle-counters) are still used.
- *Level 3* — the train notes its position by reference to a Eurobalise and informs the control centre by GSM-R radio. The control centre sends radio messages to the train, giving speed and distance in which to stop. There are no lineside signals and no track-based train detection systems. The only lineside equipment is the Eurobalise and an electronic unit.

The privatised railway has seen the introduction of many new impressive designs. Here, Class 375/5 'Electrostar' electric multiple-unit No 375624 awaits departure from Dover Priory station with the 12.06 for London Victoria on 29 October 2001. *Brian Morrison*

The evaluation of the options

The report discusses the question of cost-benefit analysis in connection with train protection systems. As has been previously mentioned, the case for ATP or ETCS at Level 1 is very weak either in terms of lives saved or in terms of operational benefits. Whilst this cost-benefit analysis has been based on historical data, ie the experience of the last 20 years, it has to be borne in mind that train speeds are increasing (and will continue to do so) and there are more trains on the system. In addition, there are many more drivers of limited experience. These factors cannot be quantified either in financial terms or in the possibility of a greater number of fatalities from SPADs but ought reasonably to be taken into account. Even then, the case for Level 1 ETCS is still weak.

However, these considerations are irrelevant; the European Directive is mandatory and is not subject to the normal HSE ranking of reducing risk to 'as low as reasonably practicable' (ALARP). The effect of this is that the government must fund the provision of ETCS, because the railway industry cannot be required to do so in cases where the application of the ALARP principle would not justify the expenditure by the railway industry. (But see the 'derogation' above.)

There remain a number of matters of concern. The availability of technical resources for installing ETCS other than on trains is limited and likely to be a defining factor in a fitment timetable unless additional resources are produced. This is an issue for both industry and the Railway Industry Training Council to deal with, but new works in signal engineering are notoriously liable to peaks and troughs of workload over a period of years and the ETCS fitment programme will have to be planned to provide a steady workload. The capacity of the supply industry should not be a problem because one of the advantages of the Technical Specifications is that they will be common throughout the industry, leading to alternative sources of supply. The ability to release rolling stock from service for fitment might be a bigger problem. Track possessions to allow fitment could present another.

The extension of BR-ATP

Short sections of the Paddington–Bristol line were deliberately omitted from the original scheme in order to observe the effect of passing from fitted to non-fitted lines, and the report recommends that they should be filled to provide continuous coverage between Paddington and Bristol. The Joint Chairmen were not persuaded that they should make any recommendation regarding the fitting of the relief lines nor of other parts of the Great Western Railtrack Zone.

There was virtual unanimity among the parties to the inquiry that any extension of train protection on lines presently equipped with BR-ATP (except as above) should be by fitment of ETCS. There was considered to be no case for fitting BR-ATP on Thames Trains using Great Western lines, taking into account the additional protection likely to be available through TPWS in the immediate future.

The Train Protection & Warning System

The report notes that TPWS would have entirely averted the Ladbroke Grove collision, since the speed of the train that passed signal No SN109 at red was modest and the overlap long. Unfortunately, it also makes the quite irrelevant observation that TPWS would have had no additional effect at Southall, as the driver had already applied the brakes. This is a commonly held misapprehension. It cannot be too frequently stated or overemphasised that AWS alone would almost certainly have intervened to prevent this collision *had it been working,* but it was isolated.

Before and during the Joint Inquiry, certain parties including the Passengers' Groups had strongly pressed for TPWS to be abandoned in favour of the earlier fitment of ETCS. They had been misled that ETCS was virtually ready to be obtained 'off the shelf', which was not the case. However, the Joint Chairmen were careful to point out that they did not accept that any decision about TPWS was inevitable.

In fact, by the time of the inquiry, the programme of TPWS trials was substantially complete and orders for the supply of equipment had been placed. The Railway Safety Regulations 1999 had mandated the date of 31 December 2003, by which time TPWS was to be in operation on both track and trains. It may seem inconceivable with the passage of time that anyone could seriously consider abandoning TPWS in favour of ETCS, but, in reality, to have done so would have condemned the railway passenger for many years to a safety system (AWS) providing no greater safety than that which was in operation at Ladbroke Grove. Within a few months after the publication of this book the TPWS fitment programme will be complete, and the twin loopholes in the AWS system which have plagued the railways for many years (the lack of any check that the driver has actually applied the brake after receiving a warning, and the passing of a signal at Danger from a standing start without realising it) will have been substantially closed.

The Joint Chairmen were at pains to stress that the fitment of TPWS should not be permitted to delay the fitment of ETCS, but the two projects are quite separate. Their anxiety was understandable but unnecessary and gives the impression of being an assurance to pressure groups, particularly as in almost the next sentence the report notes that optimistic forecasts of equipment availability are a characteristic of the railway industry. One might add that the same optimistic forecasts frequently apply to costs also.

The report has considerable reservations about the effectiveness of TPWS. However, it is not intended to be 100% effective; it is intended to increase safety, so far as SPADs or other overspeeding are concerned, by about 70%, a valuable prize which can be obtained in a relatively short time. One detects considerable concern regarding TPWS being insufficiently effective in the case of trains running at high speed (the brakes will be applied at the speed trap but the train might not stop completely within the overlap), although TPWS+ should provide some reassurance. If history is any guide, a comprehensive search of the records has failed to reveal any case of a SPAD at over 75mph causing a fatal collision *when the AWS was operative.*

Counsel for passengers' groups conceded at the end of the inquiry that: 'by the time the Joint Inquiry makes its recommendations the process of TPWS fitment would be irreversible'. In reality he was correct, although the authors of the report could not refrain from asserting their independence yet again by stating that they did not accept that their hands were tied.

The European Train Control System

The Joint Chairmen were greatly concerned that there may be delays in the fitment of ETCS and suggested that there should be regulations to make its provision mandatory by certain dates. They appear to have a view that railwaymen as a whole do not particularly want ETCS, but that is far from the case. Railwaymen want ETCS as part of a properly prepared programme taking into account all the variables, but above all they want the economies and improvements in efficiency and staff safety that will accrue from Level 2, and eventually from Level 3. They see no benefit in Level 1, because it will lead to trains being delayed and reduce line capacity.

The only people who can sensibly make a dated programme for ETCS fitment are those in the industry who are in possession of all the facts and who can prepare a comprehensive programme with all the stages listed, the workload assessed and realistic dates applied. It cannot be done otherwise. Unfortunately, this did not deter the Joint Chairmen from quoting dates by which ETCS must be fitted to specific lines. Presumably, they felt that it was expected of them but it would have been more sensible not to have done so. They produced no justification for any of the dates, which then resembled a wish-list and was of no value; indeed it was misleading. One hopes that the HSE does not fall into the same trap if it decides to make regulations. Dates which cannot be met serve little purpose, other than to create mischief. However, concern about dates is no longer relevant. The next chapter, covering the report of the ERTMS Programme Team, will provide answers.

A summary of the report's recommendations

- BR-ATP is not a serious choice for future application, but there should be some minor infilling, by extending the Chiltern system to Aynho Junction and the Great Western system to Bristol Temple Meads.

- The programme for the installation of TPWS-A should be continued. All multiple-SPAD signals should be fitted and risk assessments undertaken to establish if some high-risk, plain line signals should also be fitted. Exemptions from the TPWS Regulations should be given to some junction signals where the risk from SPADs is insignificant.

- There should be feasibility trials using additional overspeed sensors to deal with trains travelling at over 75mph (TPWS+).

- There is no recommendation regarding TPWS-E. Any decision on this is left to the industry.

- A programme should be drawn up for the fitment of ETCS, supported by Regulations being in force within three years. Annex 10 of the report gives proposed dates for the completion of trackside ETCS on the East Coast main line (by 2005 or 2006) and on the Great Western by 2006. It also recommends that all lines carrying trains at over 100mph should be fitted with ETCS by 2008.

- All new rolling stock should be compatible with ETCS and GSM-R.
- Public funding is essential and must be provided for work done under Regulations.

A view of the report

Messrs Uff and Cullen have undoubtedly made the correct recommendation to proceed with TPWS. Their recommendation also to proceed with ETCS, although a correct decision, has in any case been pre-empted by the European Commission directives.

However, the quoting of dates for the completion of fitment of ETCS to certain routes cannot be justified without the provision of a detailed staged programme of installation. At the time of the publication of the report it was not possible to say on what dates such installation might even begin. It also took for granted an adequate and timely supply of equipment and technical resources, track possessions, etc of which there is no certainty.

If any regulations are to be made (by the HSE), they must be realistic and based on a practical forecast of all factors. They must also be flexible to deal with unforeseen developments.

It is apparent from the report that the authors were concerned to demonstrate that they were paying a proper regard to the views of the pressure groups. This is understandable, given the strength of the emotions generated by this accident, but the such groups represent only their own views and have no entitlement, nor any status, to speak for the generality of the travelling public.

However, if the wish of the pressure groups that TPWS be abandoned had been granted, it is interesting to speculate what the reaction of the industry, and indeed of the HSE, would have been. Would the HSE have felt compelled to obey such a recommendation and rescind the Regulations requiring fitment, and what would have been the industry's response? The industry could not have been compelled to abandon TPWS and there is little doubt that it would have continued with its programme. To have abandoned the programme halfway through would have been irresponsible and wasteful, and no responsible railwayman could have contemplated such action.

A Class 220 Virgin 'Voyager' four-car unit, No 220020, is seen arriving at Bournemouth's recently refurbished station on 26 September 2002 on the 07.17 CrossCountry service from Manchester. These trains are visually very impressive, and the introduction of the fleet heralded a very ambitious cross-country timetable, under the title 'Operation Princess'. Some fine-tuning of the timetable has since had to be made. *Brian Morrison*

⑨ ERTMS — forward, the professionals

The history

Automatic Train Protection has been discussed at length in the previous chapters in which the reports, conclusions and recommendations of Sir David Davies' report and the Uff/Cullen report were considered. However, it should not be thought that the railway industry itself had been doing nothing on this topic whilst waiting for these reports. Quite the contrary. In the first place, ERTMS (the European Rail Traffic Management System) is a pan-European venture, and the European railway administrations are unlikely to take too much cognisance of anything that might be said in official inquiries in Britain, nor to have countenanced any delay. Secondly, Britain's railway industry and contractors have been active members of the committees and working parties involved in developing ERTMS, an involvement that certainly pre-dates Uff/Cullen/Davies. Thirdly, considerable work has been done by the industry on the practical application of ERTMS in Britain. It would have been irresponsible to have halted this important development work and done nothing until the official reports emerged.

The reader might well be puzzled by this apparent paradox. Here we have, on the one hand, official inquiries being conducted and lengthy reports being produced, whilst on the other hand the railway industry is conducting its own development work as a parallel but almost completely separate undertaking. One or other might be considered superfluous, but which one? It is the duty and responsibility of the industry to implement the European directives, co-operate in the development of ERTMS and produce a strategic plan, irrespective of any other inquiries. That is all that is necessary, but the industry has to take account of government policy, whatever that might be at the time, and the views of the Rail Safety Regulator, HM Railway Inspectorate (part of the HSE). History might rather unkindly show the official inquiries to have been irrelevant, but politically they were unavoidable. What is important is that the recommendations of those public inquiries be thoroughly considered and judged as to their appropriateness by railway professionals, who should not be afraid to say that particular recommendations are not suitable or practical for whatever reasons and will therefore not be adopted, whilst at the same time supporting those that are desirable.

Introducing the EPT

EPT is the name for the **E**uropean Rail Traffic Management System **P**rogramme **T**eam, a pan-industry body whose remit was to produce the industry plan for the implementation of ERTMS in Britain. It consisted of 50 professionals from across Europe involved in the various aspects of ERTMS and it was by far the largest team looking specifically at a national ERTMS implementation. Both sides of industry were involved — those who will supply the system and those who will buy it. Its work included extensive modelling, analysis of the safety benefits and capacity impacts of ERTMS, and a review of the development status of the system. Its final report was compiled on behalf of the ERTMS Programme Board (EPB), which was set up, and is co-chaired, by Railway Safety and the Strategic Rail Authority. It is the authoritative work on ERTMS.

What is ERTMS?

ERTMS is a modern and complex train control system that also includes Automatic Train Protection. The system was specified by the six European signalling suppliers (UNISIG) and the European railways acting together under the direction of the European Commission to achieve interoperability between track and trainborne systems. In terms of both complexity and scale the national deployment of ERTMS represents possibly the largest safety-critical control system project ever undertaken in Britain. Its impact on the operation of the railway will create a major change in both system and culture.

There are three levels of ERTMS, and each one incorporates Automatic Train Protection. They have been discussed in previous chapters, but the EPT report gives more detail and may be considered to be the definitive version:

Level 1

This is the simplest form and consists of trackside equipment which 'reads' the signal aspects being shown and passes the information to the train via track-mounted transponders, called balises. The information being transmitted is received by an on-board computer that determines the speed at which the train may run in order to obey the signal aspects being shown. It also supervises the speed and intervenes if it exceeds the appropriate computer-assessed speed.

There are two variants. System 'A' has one balise for each signal, but the on-board computer is only updated when the train passes over a balise. Its disadvantage is that the driver may be able to see that the signal ahead has changed to a less restrictive aspect long before he reaches the balise, but he cannot respond to it until the computer is updated. This causes unnecessary delays and in congested areas can result in a significant reduction in line capacity.

System 'B' is similar to System 'A' but provides an 'infill' (an additional balise) some distance before reaching the other balise in order to update the onboard computer more quickly.

This reduces but does not eliminate delays, but significantly increases the cost.

Level 1 has no benefit other than to provide ATP. As has been shown previously, the cost of Level 1, some £3 billion, cannot possibly be justified in terms of fatalities avoided, about two per year. The emotional pressures for ATP following Ladbroke Grove were irrational, because TPWS currently being fitted would have prevented that accident.

Level 1 retains all the existing features of train signalling and control, ie the signalling system and the train detection systems (track circuits and axle-counters), together with all their associated costs, both for maintenance and renewal.

Level 2

Track-based train detection systems are still used, but the information normally given to the driver by means of lineside signals is replaced by information about the state of the line ahead given to him on the console in his driving cab. This information is transmitted from a Radio Block Centre, which is in effect a computerised signalbox that knows where all trains are. That knowledge enables it to calculate how far ahead the line is clear for any particular train. Information sent to trains is continuously updated.

Level 2 has three variants, called 'systems'.

- System 'C' retains lineside signals, mainly for the benefit of the drivers of trains that are not equipped with ERTMS. This will be a temporary phase, lasting only until all trains needing to pass over a particular route are equipped with ERTMS. It may also be appropriate to retain signals on a semi-permanent basis in congested areas. This will undoubtedly be considered further during implementation, after some experience has been gained in operating trains without lineside signals. A further reason for retaining lineside signals is to provide a 'back-up' in case of system failure. This ought not to be necessary; the system should be sufficiently robust, and provided with duplicate facilities, to enable it to continue to operate under any circumstances. It should be as robust as the

The 15.40 ESW freight train, No 6M99, conveying steel bars from Immingham to Wolverhampton Steel Terminal, passes through Stoke-on-Trent behind Class 66 diesel-electric locomotive No 66035. *Brian Morrison*

operation and control systems used in the aviation industry.

The retention of lineside signals may produce a confliction to drivers of trains equipped with Level 2. They would expect to drive with complete reliance on their in-cab displays but this could conflict with the lineside signals. One would expect this issue to be resolved before ERTMS is introduced, but it would seem sensible for the driver to drive solely on his in-cab display and ignore the lineside signals at all times, even when a lineside signal displays a more restrictive aspect than is indicated by his in-cab display. It would surely be a nonsense for a driver to be required to drive in accordance with the aspects being displayed by lineside signals; he would then have to ignore the in-cab display which, having been provided at great expense, would cease to have much value.

- System 'D' normally dispenses with lineside signals and relies entirely on 'cab signalling'. This is a major advance. It avoids the conflict which exists in System 'C', but more importantly it avoids all the costs, both in materials and manpower, associated with the provision, maintenance and renewal of lineside signals and their supporting structures. It avoids the need for signal technicians to go on or near the track and it avoids the delays that occur during failures of signalling equipment. Lineside signalling is operated through lineside cabling, which is expensive and prone to accidental or wanton damage, causing severe and protracted train delays. There are many good reasons for dispensing with lineside signals; indeed, if suitable technology had existed in the early days of railways to provide cab signalling, they would never have been invented.

Emergency equipment in the driving cab ready for immediate use. Detonators and red flags may seem like relics of yesteryear but still have their uses. Track circuit operating clips are a more recent invention and can place signals to red in an emergency. In Level 3 of ERTMS there are no track circuits and total reliance will have to be placed on radio communication. However, Level 3 installations are likely to be many years in the future.
D. C. Hall

GSM-R radio would be used for passing messages to and from trains and would replace the National Radio Network and the Cab Secure Radio system in due course.

- There is a System 'E' with much reduced trackside infrastructure for use on lightly used regional lines. It would be similar to the existing Radio Electronic Token Block system.

Level 3

Level 3 builds on Level 2, but provides safety-critical train position by radio. It avoids the need for conventional train detection systems, such as track circuits and axle-counters, with their attendant provision, maintenance and renewal costs.

Track circuits have reached the limit of their technical development, although they have formed the essential bedrock of modern signalling systems. Unfortunately, problems have arisen in recent years in obtaining reliable train detection at all times, due to imperfect electrical conductivity between the wheel and the rail. Rail surface conditions may deteriorate due to contamination from rust, dirt and other deposits such as leaf mulch, which is caused by leaves falling on damp rails and being crushed by the wheels of passing trains. Track circuits are becoming increasingly unreliable in the detection of certain types of modern multiple-units and lightweight vehicles, with particular problems being experienced with Class 158 diesel multiple-units.

Track circuits are of very ancient lineage. They were invented in the United States of America in 1872, but did not find favour in Britain for many years, although there were isolated installations before the end of the 19th century. They were primarily provided as a safety measure to guard against signalmen forgetting the presence of a train at or near their signalbox.

Whilst track circuits are prone to right-side failures which cause train delays, they have a number of incidental advantages:

- A device called a track-circuit operating clip is carried on every train for use in an emergency. It consists of two clips connected by a piece of wire long enough to stretch from one rail to another. When the clips are applied to both rails of a line, the track circuit is actuated, which has the effect of placing the signal in

rear to Danger. It is a useful safety device, although the availability of radio communication now provides an alternative means of securing the safety of the line.

- A broken rail, where the break is complete, may be detected by a track circuit, which will place the signal in rear to Danger. However, there are track circuits on electrified lines where the track circuit operates on only one of the two rails. There are other means for detecting broken rails.

- An obstruction of the line, depending on its nature, may be detected by a track circuit. There is no practical alternative, other than the use of radio, provided the appropriate railway authority can be contacted quickly.

Axle-counters, whilst having none of the incidental advantages of track circuits mentioned above, are now often the preferred alternative. An axle-counter records electronically each axle that passes the counting heads fixed to the web of the rail. An axle-counter section of line has counting heads at the entrance and exit of a section and the two counts must agree before the section can be considered clear.

Applications of Level 3 are several, possibly many, years in the future, and there is no direct work on Level 3 in Europe being done at the time of writing. However, the potential benefits of Level 3, in engineering, operations and financial terms, are considerable. They include what is called 'Moving Block', a system in which the existing concept of a fixed block system, where the railway line is divided into 'blocks' of various lengths, is abandoned. A fixed block system is another relic of the early days of railways, and requires a block section and its safety overlap to be clear before another train can be admitted to it, irrespective of the length of that block section. With 'Moving Block', trains can in theory be allowed to run at braking distance apart (plus a safety margin).

Given the above, it seems incredible now that Railtrack in its younger, more confident, days actually envisaged a Level 3 application for the West Coast main line modernisation. Events have proved it to be over-confidence. Level 3 appears to be a long way in the future.

What are the main benefits of ERTMS?

So far as the mainland of Europe is concerned, the main benefit is expected to be improved interoperability, enabling

Yet another new design of train, a Class 458 'Juniper' electric multiple-unit, No 8005, is seen arriving at Woking with the 09.47 from Basingstoke to Waterloo on 22 October 2001. *Brian Morrison*

trains to operate across Europe safely and effectively under a common control system, creating in effect a pan-Europe network. This will improve train operation, with the main benefit likely to be felt in the operation of freight trains. It is essential to speed up freight transits if rail is to retain its share of the market and, desirably, increase it. The European Commission is very keen to see this happen. Improved inter-operability is likely to have very little impact on the passenger business in Britain but faster and more reliable freight transits have the potential to lead to a substantial transfer of cross-Channel freight from road to rail.

The signal equipment manufacturing companies involved will produce equipment to a common specification, and competition between them might be expected to result in higher standards, greater availability and lower prices.

ERTMS in Britain is expected to have the following benefits at the higher levels:

- The abolition of lineside signals will reduce signalling costs, including maintenance, and avoid the delays caused by signalling failures.

- Train location reporting will no longer depend on track circuits, which are prone to failure. Delays caused by equipment failures will no longer occur.

- Drivers will drive their trains with greater confidence by the certainty which a signal in the cab will provide. They will no longer have to look ahead to identify their own signal and react correctly to its message in all weathers. This will be particularly helpful in complex layouts and at high speeds.

The safety of train operation will be enhanced by the provision of Automatic Train Protection as an integral part of ERTMS. However, it is important to stress that TPWS will significantly reduce ATP-preventable risks (and will be doing so by the end of 2003), leaving only a small additional risk to be dealt with by ERTMS. It is equally important to point out that the cost of ERTMS could not be justified purely as a safety investment to reduce train accidents still further. It is the other benefits that will ultimately make investment in ERTMS worthwhile, provided that the work is carried out in a properly staged and programmed manner.

The preferred solution of the ERTMS Programme Team

The ERTMS Programme Team recognises that implementing Level 1 would bring few benefits, but would have severe cost implications, as well as operational disbenefits. It is not an option that could be seriously considered by the industry. The preferred option is Level 2 without lineside signals (System D), partly because it would bring the greatest benefits, and partly because Level 3 is not likely to be available in a reasonable timescale. However, Level 2 can be achieved only with the installation of new computer-based interlockings, which in turn means that installation can economically and sensibly take place only when existing signalling systems are due for replacement, or where there is a special case for accelerating replacement.

The development timetable

Although ERTMS is similar in concept to ATP systems already in operation, it has the major difference that Level 2 requires GSM-R telecommunications. This remains the major technical risk. There is also significant development work remaining, and System D is still under development and testing in mainland Europe. In Switzerland, there is a Level 2 trial project over a 35km stretch of the Olten–Lucerne main line of Swiss Federal Railways (SBB) between Zofingen and Sempach, which began in April 2002. There have been difficulties, particularly with data transmission between track and train, and when the Radio Block Centre 'crashed' on September 15, SBB admitted that it was worried as so many things were going wrong and people were starting to lose faith in the system. SBB recognises that there is still a long way to go, but has committed itself to installing ETCS on all main lines by 2017. That programme was intended to begin with the new line between Mattstetten and Rothrist, due to open in December 2004, but the current problems with ETCS prompted SBB to set up a task force in October 2002 to determine future policy on ETCS and whether or not a back-up system should be installed on the new line. That back-up system would probably have to be a conventional system.

SBB is determined to ensure that the line can be opened for commercial service on time in 2004 without being at the mercy of an ETCS system that is less than 100% reliable.

German Railways (DB) expresses some doubt about the value to it of ETCS, given that it already has satisfactory train protection systems, such as the LZB inductive train control system, which are substantially cheaper. It says that there is no commercial incentive to install ETCS and that it will require state funding to meet its high capital cost. However, European Union standards will require ETCS on Germany's high-speed lines, and DB is planning to take part in trials of ETCS Level 2 on part of the line between Berlin, Halle and Leipzig. Trial operations are not expected before the end of 2003.

Siemens Transportation Systems has stated that state-of-the-art onboard equipment is now available, but sounds a warning that meeting national requirements and integrating ERTMS/ETCS onboard equipment into the environment of a locomotive or train is not a simple task. That caveat cannot be over-emphasised, as BR learned to its cost when attempting to develop BR-ATP in the early 1990s.

Other risks include cost escalation and the shortage of resources, particularly of engineers with the required skills. However, both the Strategic Rail Authority and the railway industry itself are developing plans to deal with the expected shortage of engineers. Perhaps the main strategic risk is the occurrence of another catastrophic ATP-preventable accident leading to pressures to accelerate installation to obtain ATP benefits, regardless of cost or consequences. One would hope that in such an event the government would stand firm, supported by such organisations as the SRA, the Rail Regulator and even the HSE. However, it should be pointed out that prior to Ladbroke Grove there had never been a previous catastrophic SPAD of such severity on an AWS-equipped line, and that TPWS will reduce that risk by up to 80%.

The Programme Team has reviewed all the factors and has confirmed the need for a programme of further system development. This will cover among other things:

First phase

- ERTMS-ready specifications for new equipment.
- Validation of route capacity .
- Operational rules and signalling principles.
- Preparation of feasibility designs.
- Preparation of business cases for specific routes.
- Taking account of SRA enhancements.
- Taking account of Train Operators' plans.
- Telecommunications design for GSM-R.

Planning work so far undertaken indicates that high-performance ERTMS is not expected to be proven as a wholly reliable total system ready for national implementation in Britain until about 2008, which indicates the wisdom of continuing to install TPWS and develop TPWS+.

Second phase

The report lists the following principles:

- Guidance given by the ERTMS Planning Board setting out the priorities for installing ERTMS on high-speed and high-density routes, and maximising the use of higher level ERTMS.

- Fitting ERTMS Level 2 to trains, depending on the routes they use, and taking the opportunity to remove lineside signals upon resignalling where possible.

- Fitting trackside equipment with or without lineside signals, depending on the type of interlocking and the dates for its renewal.

- Synchronising the fitting of ERTMS with Network Rail's signalling renewals programme where possible, and planning renewals on the basis of doing a whole route.

- Implementing GSM-R with data capacity for ERTMS Level 2.

- Planning a predictable and continuous programme of work over clear timescales, with funding allocated, on which the industry can base its recruitment and training programme and on which the supply industry can plan its production.

- A co-ordinating organisation that crosses track-to-train boundaries (what would at one time have been called a 'Project Manager' but which is now referred to as a 'System Authority'. A System Authority is an *ad hoc* organisation established to manage and oversee a whole project).

The report goes on to make the important point that further work is required in the development phase before realistic timescales can be set. Perhaps this should have been set out in large print in order to warn various regulatory agencies against the danger of attempting to set target dates at this stage. Professor Uff and Lord Cullen unfortunately fell into this trap in their otherwise generally satisfactory report into train protection systems, although they did include a caveat about target dates being 'subject to many variables' and 'dependent on a number of factors'. In view of the latter, it might have been more judicious to have resisted the temptation to set target dates.

The report's recommendations

1. The SRA and the industry should continue to support the Total System Development Programme over its anticipated duration. Appropriate priority should be given to standards and specifications for new trains and signalling so that these can be provided as 'ERTMS-ready'.

2. A System Authority should be created, including a technical team to support deployment of ERTMS and a team to lead the ERTMS project and associated procurement on a national basis.

3. An examination should be carried out to determine what additional measures over and above TPWS might be required at high-risk locations until ERTMS is commissioned. In view of the apparent probability that 10 years or more may elapse before ERTMS is installed at such high-risk locations, this is an important proviso. TPWS+ could provide the answer in most cases. (But first define your high-risk location! It is unlikely that Wembley, Purley, Cowden or Watford Junction would have fallen within that definition unless the net were cast very wide. TPWS or TPWS+ would cater for all four.)

4. The SRA should continue to specify and fund early deployment consistent with the strategic plan.

To sum up

It is clear that ERTMS throughout Europe is going to be very expensive, and that funding will have to be provided by member governments which are probably not yet aware of just how much funding might ultimately be required. However, the benefits accruing from interoperability are potentially great if they allow railborne freight to travel throughout Europe with the freedom presently enjoyed by roadborne freight. The ATP component is mainly a factor in Britain, because most Continental railways already have better train protection systems than Britain, at least until the installation of TPWS is complete. However, even in Britain the potential avoidance of fatalities under ERTMS is only about two per year on average, at a huge cost per fatality.

The report demonstrates the long timescale before implementation of ERTMS in Britain can begin. This was always likely to be the case, given the history of previous similar ventures, but the possibility seems to have been overlooked by many, who assumed without any proof that implementation could begin as soon as Uff and Cullen had spoken. The report hazards no guesses as to the duration of the fitment programme once implementation begins, but it seems likely to be well over 10 years and could easily be 20. The work done by the ERTMS Programme Team exposes the fundamental weakness of the Uff/Cullen report, and indeed the folly of commissioning such a report. Messrs Uff and Cullen were not to blame. They did their best with the information presented to them but it was faulty in some cases and incomplete in others. It should have been left to the professionals but politics intruded and both the government and the HSE were weak and ineffective in the face of a hostile media. There was no 'Mr Railway' to defend the industry, but even if there had been, the history of former BR chairmen in fighting the industry's corner in such circumstances has not been encouraging. The malign influence of the fear of prosecution by either the British Transport Police or the HSE has been all too clearly demonstrated.

The Programme Team has established that there is no rational case for investing billions of pounds simply to avoid the small residual risk posed by the limitations of TPWS, and that train protection benefits are incidental to the justification for ERTMS. Indeed, The Railways (Interoperability) (High-Speed) Regulations 2002, previously mentioned, provide an important safeguard on the issue of costs, which could be especially relevant to conventional lines. It will be recalled that ERTMS is only required to be installed when signalling is renewed or routes are upgraded. If the application of ERTMS might compromise the economic viability of such a project, a derogation might be given allowing the project to go ahead without such fitment. Applications for derogation have to be submitted in the first place to the Strategic Rail Authority, who will then seek the advice of HSE on the safety implications and the Office of the Rail Regulator on the economic aspects. The application for derogation then has to be submitted to the European Commission for approval.

The benefits of ERTMS will accrue when Level 2 without lineside signals is fully developed, and when train detection and positioning can be achieved by radio instead of by track circuits and other detection devices, at Level 3. The installation of ERTMS system-wide will be a huge undertaking, and no one should underestimate the complexities involved. It will require unremitting commitment from all parties, from the government itself downwards, through the SRA to the whole of industry. It will also require guaranteed funding over many years. A challenge indeed.

Postscript

On 14 January 2003 the HSE published three reports which it had commissioned from consultancies into the EPT report. The reports dealt with (1) economic aspects, (2) technical aspects, and (3) public dialogue. The following conclusions emerged:

- There does not appear to be sufficient justification for the early fitment of ERTMS/ETC on the grounds of ATP safety benefits alone.
- The provision of Level 1 cannot be justified.
- There is no incremental path from Level 1 to Level 2.
- The underlying level of ATP-preventable risk should be estimated from past data.
  [Author's note: From 1970 to 1999 169 passengers were killed by train accidents from all causes — approximately 5.6 per year on average. Errors by drivers caused 78 of those deaths — around 2.5 per year on average. TPWS and TPWS+ should reduce that number to one per year, which agrees with the EPT figure. The consultants believe that passenger fatalities could be even rarer than that, indeed, since 1980 there has not been one SPAD-induced passenger fatality that did not have the potential to have been avoided by TPWS/TPWS+. And as a matter of interest, in the last half-century the drivers of East Coast main line expresses have caused only one passenger fatality by passing a signal at Danger, and that would have been prevented by AWS!]
- The fitment timetable recommended by the Uff/Cullen Inquiry is not viable.
- The industry's preference for Level 2 System D is supported.
- Passengers are more concerned about anti-social behaviour than the likelihood of being involved in a train accident.
- Passengers believed that the fragmented nature of the industry and the lack of clear leadership and strategy inhibited the development of safety strategies.
- There is an implied view that ERTMS installation should be delayed until existing signalling is life-expired.

The HSE then wrote to the Secretary of State on 2 February 2003 confirming its advice on the best way forward for developing and installing effective Automatic Train Protection (ATP) on Britain's railways. The HSE accepts the consultancies' findings that the Uff/Cullen timetable for fitment is not valid, and believes that the current state of technology renders a timetable inappropriate. It does not believe that it is practicable to insist on ERTMS at present. The HSE does not support Level 1, but it endorses Level 2, and considers that the industry must press ahead with the development and installation of ERTMS. It also believes that the use of H&S law to mandate ERTMS is not very appropriate. These are very sensible conclusions.

10 The Ladbroke Grove Rail Inquiry — Part 2 Report

The nature of the inquiry — back to Lord Cullen

As mentioned earlier, following the collisions at Ladbroke Grove Junction on 5 October 1999, the Rt Hon Lord Cullen was appointed by the Health & Safety Commission, with the consent of the Deputy Prime Minister (as part of his Transport responsibilities), to conduct a public inquiry (under Sec 14(2)(b) of the Health & Safety at Work etc Act 1974).

In view of the breadth of the inquiry and the many factors involved, Lord Cullen decided to deal with the matter in three parts. Part 1 is discussed in Chapter 6 and Train Protection Systems in Chapter 8. This chapter deals with Part 2, the remit of which was as follows:

'To consider general experience derived from relevant accidents on the railway since the Hidden Inquiry (into the Clapham accident in 1988), with a view to drawing conclusions about:
a) factors which affect safety management
b) the appropriateness of the current regulatory regime.
In the light of the above, to make recommendations for improving safety on the future railway.'

Robert Owen QC continued as counsel to the inquiry. Professor Peter H. McKie CBE, formerly Chairman of DuPont (UK), and Mr Malcolm J. Southgate, formerly Deputy Managing Director of Eurostar (UK), continued as assessors.

The hearings of the inquiry, which was held at the Central Hall, Westminster, began on 31 October 2000 and finished on 20 December the same year. The evidence was presented by the following parties:

- Collins Passengers' Group (representing injured and bereaved in the accident).
- Southall and Ladbroke Grove Solicitors' Group (also representing the injured and bereaved).
- The Joint Rail Unions.
- The Association of Train Operating Companies.
- The Rail Users' Consultative Committees.
- Railtrack.
- The Health & Safety Commission and the Health & Safety Executive.
- The Strategic Rail Authority.
- The Rail Regulator.
- The British Transport Police.
- Amey Rail.
- The Rolling Stock Leasing Companies.
- The English, Welsh & Scottish Railway (the freight operating company).
- The Railway Industry Association.

The procedure adopted was the same as at Lord Cullen's other inquiries. Each witness appeared in turn, to be questioned by the inquiry counsel, then cross-examined by any or all of the parties represented. It was a judicial inquiry. Fifty-four witnesses appeared and gave evidence, and a further eight provided written evidence. With so many parties represented, and with so many witnesses involved, it can readily be appreciated why the inquiry lasted for so long. Ultimately, there were hundreds of ring binders of evidence, which must have weighed many tonnes, and it is greatly to Lord Cullen's credit that he managed to absorb the material and produce a thorough and mainly well-founded report. To assist him, he separated the content of the inquiry into six headings:

- The Regulatory Authority (the HSE).
- Railtrack and the Safety & Standards Directorate (subsequently known as Railway Safety Ltd, and then simply Railway Safety).
- The safety case regime.
- The relationship between the constituent parts of the industry.
- The management of safety.
- Railway accident investigation.

In order to cast the net as wide as possible, Lord Cullen arranged for a questionnaire dealing with these issues to be available so that anyone interested could give his or her views.

The regulatory authority (HSE)

The Health & Safety Executive is the executive arm of the commission. It has many spheres of interest, of which railways are but one (but probably the most high profile). It acquired its interest in railways when it absorbed the Railway Inspectorate (RI) in 1990. The RI had formerly been a small section within the Department of Transport indeed it had been part of the Transport Department since its formation in 1919 as the Ministry of Transport. Prior to that, it had been part of the Board of Trade since its formation in 1840.

The RI had always been a small section, consisting of a Chief Inspecting Officer and three or four Inspecting Officers, supported by a small administrative group. It was formed to examine new railways to ensure that they were safe for the carriage of passengers, but it investigated the more serious accidents from its inception. Following the passage of the Railways (Prevention of Accidents) Act in 1900 it formed a small group of Railway Employment Inspectors who investigated accidents to staff. The Railway Inspectorate's duties were broadly:

- To examine new works to ensure that they were safe for passengers.

- To investigate accidents and make appropriate recommendations.
- To give advice to ministers on appropriate railway issues.

The last coach of the 'Thames Turbo' lies on its side at Ladbroke Grove next to the relatively undamaged centre section of the HST. The first coach of the 'Turbo' has been completely wrecked. *Duncan Phillips*

It is important to be aware of the limits of its responsibilities. It performed an audit function on the railways so far as safety performance was concerned. It did not supervise the current working of the railways at all, nor did it carry out examinations or inspections. They were not part of its role. This was clearly not understood in the late 1980s, when it was wrongly criticised for not taking action over an unsatisfactory safety issue at King's Cross (LTE) in 1987, regarding the maintenance of the escalators. This resulted in a serious fire in which many people were killed.

Hard on its heels came the Clapham accident in 1988 when again there were some invalid criticisms that the RI was not sufficiently active, although there is no way in which the RI can be accused of any shortcomings at Clapham. There were accusations that the relationship between the RI and the railway industry was 'too cosy'. In fact, that was a complete misinterpretation of the situation. Relationships between the RI and the railways were very good, because they were based on mutual understanding, trust and respect for each other's expertise and knowledge. The RI was held in very high esteem by the railway industry.

However, the insinuations of 'cosiness' would not go away, as a result of which the RI was transferred to the HSE in 1990, to be renamed HM Railway Inspectorate (HMRI). Cosiness was not part of the HSE's agenda, but it did not immediately demand any major change in HMRI's attitude to the railways (it was still British Rail at this stage). However, gradually over the years there appeared a more proactive, aggressive approach and the rigorous application of the Health & Safety at Work Act. The HSE was simply keen to deal with the railways as with any other industry, and it failed to recognise that railways are very different from other industries. As the HSE's attitude changed, so the good work done by the RI over many generations in establishing a productive relationship with the railways was destroyed. Mutual suspicion and threats (from the HSE) replaced trust and respect. HMRI expanded enormously, with the creation of field inspectorates to carry out proactive inspections, but experienced, qualified staff were hard to obtain and they were never available in sufficient numbers for the new workload. Some existing, well-qualified inspectors left. They were replaced by an increased number of staff well-versed in HSE practices but with little or no knowledge of the workings of railways. It was known as 'brigading', and was the nadir of the fortunes of HMRI.

Almost all the witnesses at the inquiry criticised the performance of the HSE in its stewardship of HMRI and asserted that it was in effect not a suitable home for HMRI. It was said that the HSE had culpably failed to provide HMRI with sufficient staff of the proper calibre and with the necessary railway experience and technical qualifications. Witnesses recommended that it should be removed from the HSE and established as an independent safety regulator for the railways. There were only two dissenting voices among the host of witnesses supporting this course of action. Predictably, one was the HSE. However, Lord Cullen was not convinced. Flying in the face of this mass of evidence (surely an unusual, not to say unprecedented, course of action for an

Above:
A reminder that not all accidents are caused by faulty permanent way or drivers passing signals at danger. The earth slip just north of Ais Gill derailed a Class 156 DMU on its way to Carlisle. A collision then ensued in which the conductor lost his life. Since this derailment, which occurred on 31 January 1995, Railtrack carried out substantial works both on the Settle–Carlisle line and elsewhere to prevent such slips. *Author's collection*

Below:
The wrecked front end of an EMU near Greenock, caused by vandalism. The train became derailed by an obstruction on the line and collided with a bridge abutment, killing the driver. Vandalism is becoming one of the most frequent causes of accidents. *Author's collection*

eminent lawyer) he recommended that HMRI should remain a part of the HSE, partly for the odd reason that a small HMRI safety regulator standing alone might be 'captured' by the railway industry. Shades of fear of the 'cosy' relationship re-emerging! Lord Cullen overlooked, and was presumably quite unaware, that the much smaller RI had never been captured by the railways at any time in its 150 years' existence. However, the die was cast.

There was one small crumb of comfort. Cullen recognised that the HSE's stewardship of HMRI had been inefficient, and some have implied that HMRI did not make its case sufficiently strongly. Cullen proposed that HMRI should be placed under the direction of a new post, to be filled by a person of outstanding managerial ability, not necessarily with a railway background, and with a special salary level. Yet again, we have this apparent belief that no knowledge of the varied intricacies of the railway industry in all its many facets is necessary to regulate its safety. The implication is that any Tom, Dick or Harry can do it, provided he is a good manager. Would Lord Cullen say the same about the nuclear power industry, or the oil industry, or the chemical industry? (Or the legal profession? Perhaps a good manager could become Lord Chief Justice?)

However, Lord Cullen's recommendation No 36 has already been adopted. Alan Osborne has been appointed to the new post of Director of Railway Safety at the HSE and took up his new duties on 1 November 2002. He is responsible for HMRI and is a member of the HSE Board. Fortunately, Mr Osborne has some experience of railways, having been with London Underground for six years, including three as Safety and Quality Director. None the less, he will find the main line railways a bigger challenge than London Underground. And finally, in Recommendation No 35 Lord Cullen states bluntly that it is imperative that the HSE be provided with adequate resources to fulfil its role through HMRI. This is a pointed criticism of the HSC for not doing so previously. However, it remains to be seen whether the HSC will respond and provide adequate resources of inspectors technically qualified in the various aspects of railway engineering and operations. (Cullen refers to it as 'personnel who have the relevant experience and expertise in regard to the railways'.) But even if the will is there, the HSE may find it difficult to recruit and retain such staff. There is a national shortage of technically qualified engineers with railway experience and there are plenty of other openings for them.

Railtrack and railway safety

There are a number of aphorisms that have caused damage to the railway industry's reputation. 'The wrong kind of snow' is a phrase that was coined by a journalist, but in popular mythology was uttered by an unfortunate railwayman. A more recent one is 'Profits before safety'. It is a silly, meaningless phrase, but had enormous impact. Without profits, there would be no funds to invest in safety. Indeed, without profits no private-sector industry can survive. However, the damage was done.

Railtrack was the butt of the 'Profits before safety' tag, mainly because its Safety & Standards Directorate (S&SD) was responsible for setting safety standards. By implication Railtrack was more concerned with profits than safety, but it was in a very similar position to the pre-nationalisation

railway companies (pre-1948), which had always had to balance expenditure on safety against all the other demands on its funds. Part of the problem was the nature of privatisation.

The position which Railtrack occupied as 'Infrastructure Controller' had its origin in the report 'Ensuring Safety on Britain's Railways', produced by the HSC in 1993 to assist the government in framing the Railways Bill. That report said that:

'For a potential new operator [later known as a Train Operator] running a service on the national infrastructure . . . that operator must be held accountable for those aspects for which he has control. But because that operator might be introducing risk into the railway environment which could affect the safety of the infrastructure . . . there must also be a responsibility upon the party who has control of the system [ie Railtrack] to impose conditions upon access.'

Railtrack was to be a permanent player, the owner and controller of the infrastructure, and responsible under HSE law for ensuring as far as possible that the train operators (not permanent, but semi-transient bodies) which were granted access to Railtrack's infrastructure ran their trains safely. Hence Railtrack, as the permanent body and responsible for

An aerial view of the result of a collision at Rickerscote, near Stafford, on 8 March 1996 between a derailed freight train and a Travelling Post Office train. One Royal Mail employee was killed. The derailment was caused by a complete fracture of one of the axles of a wagon in the freight train. *Author's collection*

safety on its infrastructure, was considered to be the proper authority for setting safety standards. Railtrack maintained that it could not discharge its responsibilities for safety under HSE law unless it controlled the setting of safety standards.

However, there were strident calls and media pressures to sever the connection between Railtrack's operations and the S&SD. There were political pressures, too, and a cosmetic change was made. The S&SD was renamed Railway Safety Ltd to give the impression that it was no longer part of Railtrack. In fact, it still belonged to Railtrack but organisationally it became a stand-alone unit. Railway Safety became a wholly-owned subsidiary of Railtrack Group PLC with a separate board to increase the independence of the activities of the S&SD and separate them from the commercial interests of its parent, Railtrack.

That restructuring did not satisfy the demands for a transparent severance of the ownership of Railway Safety by Railtrack. Most parties at the inquiry argued strongly for such a complete severance, partly on the grounds that safety was an intrinsic concern of all parties in the industry. Railtrack countered by stating that if it could not control safety through the Railway Group Standards published by Railway Safety it could not meet its responsibilities under HSE law regarding safety on its infrastructure.

The alternative submitted by several parties was to the effect that Railway Safety's activities and responsibilities should be exercised by a new organisation representing all parties in the industry, in effect subsuming Railway Safety. Lord Cullen accepted this view. Discussion then centred on the nature of that new body, and to whom it should belong, or whether it should be free-standing. He was clear in his mind that it should not be part of the HSE, because he felt quite firmly that the setting of safety standards was the responsibility of the industry. Only the industry had the range of knowledge and experience required for the task, and being closely in touch with day-to-day events was an essential requirement.

Lord Cullen made 17 recommendations on this subject, the most important of which were:

- The function of setting Railway Group Standards should be assumed by a new rail industry body (known as the Rail Industry Safety Body — RISB) which is independent of both Railtrack Group PLC and its subsidiaries and of the safety regulator (ie HSE). It should be set up as a new legal entity. *[Author's comment — this ensures the new body's complete independence of any railway company, which was the objective.]*

- The governance of the new body should have representation from railway operators, manufacturers and suppliers of infrastructure equipment and rolling stock, and the three main rail trade unions. It should have an independent chairman and a number of independent members with suitable practical experience. *[Author's comment — the new body must have a continuous feedback from all parts of the industry if it is to function effectively, and suitable liaison arrangements below governance level will be essential. This is vitally important and the governing body must ensure that the feedback and liaison arrangements work effectively. The purpose of having an independent chairman is to assist in the resolving of any disputes within the governing body.]*

- The RISB should also exercise a number of other functions, including:

  1) Establishing and managing system authorities. *[Author's comment — These are created to provide a means of funding and managing new schemes which involve several companies.]*
  2) Funding and sponsoring research and development. *[Author's comment — There has been inadequate provision for this in the privatised railway structure, but on 25 February 2003 a new centre for railway research was inaugurated. Rail Research UK is being established by the Engineering and Physical Sciences Research Council to provide a 'one stop shop of knowledge' encompassing 12 research groups from seven universities and will be operational from April 2003.]*

  3) Monitoring and reporting on the industry's safety performance.
  4) Providing safety leadership. *[Author's comment — this has been a glaring omission in the privatised railway, and the situation has always been unsatisfactory, particularly in media participation following serious accidents. There has been no one to speak responsibly and collectively for the railway industry on safety matters, a sort of 'Mr Railway'. The gap has been filled by various spokesmen, but primarily by Railtrack. Now one assumes that the lead will be taken by the chairman of the RISB. One of his more important attributes will be the need to be good on television.]*

This section of the report is excellent and demonstrates Lord Cullen's penetrating insight at its best.

The new organisation is expected to be operational by early summer 2003. It will be called the 'Railway Safety and Standards Board' (RSSB).

The safety case

In the prelude to privatisation, the government was concerned about the effect upon safety of the creation of a large number of new companies, which may have little or no prior knowledge of railway operations, and which may conduct their operations with a less than sufficient regard for safety. This could be a particular problem if a company's profits were declining and it attempted to reduce costs in a manner inconsistent with a high standard of safety. In order to guard against this, the HSE was asked to consider the situation and advise the government on the steps that should be taken.

The principle of the safety case was already established in the oil and chemical industries (indeed, Lord Cullen himself had introduced safety cases in the oil industry following the Piper Alpha oil-rig disaster), and the HSE recommended that it should be applied to the privatised railway industry. Railtrack's safety case should be approved by the HSE, whilst the safety cases of the Train Operators should be approved by Railtrack in its role as custodian of the infrastructure. Lord Cullen considered whether any changes should be made to that structure.

The preparation of a safety case requires the identification of every significant risk associated with a company's activities, and a statement of the means by which those risks could be reduced to a level 'as low as reasonably practicable'. It was a very reasonable safeguard in the context of a new fragmented railway industry. However, a number of parties to the inquiry questioned both its value and its continuing necessity, pointing out that such a regime was not appropriate for ongoing day-to-day operations where the risks of existing systems were already known and understood. It was suggested that operators too often relied upon experts for the writing of their safety cases, which tended to be written in a manner driven primarily by the need to comply with the requirements of the regulations. They also tended to detract from management's responsibility.

The privatised railway has now been in existence for several years and the fears of irresponsible behaviour on the part of railway operators have not been borne out. Safety cases were never necessary on BR, nor had such a system ever been considered for application to the pre-nationalised

railways. The safety case regime has outlived its usefulness on the railways and should be abandoned. It is a piece of unnecessary bureaucracy and an inadequate substitute for effective and experienced management. Unfortunately, Lord Cullen was not to be persuaded. However, as a separate issue, Railtrack has been relieved of its responsibilities for approving train operators' safety cases; this has been transferred to the HSE, resulting in the requirement for a large number of new posts in that organisation. This rather neatly demonstrates the degree of bureaucracy involved in the safety case system.

Ladbroke Grove, 4 October 1999. The total destruction of the leading car of the 'Thames Turbo' unit is graphically shown in this photograph. Nineteen of its 25 passengers lost their lives. The HST Mk 3 coach alongside appears to have survived remarkably well, as did its passengers, although several were injured. Only six passengers were killed in the HST, all in the front coach. The train itself conveyed 422 passengers and staff. Once again, the splendid crashworthiness of the 25-year-old Mk 3 coaches on the HSTs was demonstrated, a great tribute to its BR designers. *Modern Railways*

Accident investigation

There are a number of organisations and bodies currently interested in the investigation of accidents, the purpose of which is to ascertain the cause. These include railway companies, the HSE and possibly the British Transport Police. The primary purpose of identifying the cause is to enable measures to be taken to guard against a recurrence, or to reduce its likelihood.

The HSE is involved, owing to its role as the safety regulator. It needs to know about the occurrence of accidents so that it can:

- decide whether it requires a full report;

- maintain a comprehensive record so that it can identify and monitor trends;

- satisfy itself that the necessary remedial action has been taken;

- consider whether there has been an offence under the Health & Safety at Work Act, and whether prosecution is justified.

The BT Police is interested in case the cause of the accident constitutes a criminal offence. Manslaughter is the usual charge if there have been fatalities, but in other cases the charge may be endangering the safety of passengers, under the Offences Against the Person Act 1861. The latter Act was invoked against the driver of the train involved in the derailment at Morpeth on 24 June 1984.

In BR days there was a well-established routine for reporting and investigating railway accidents. All accidents except those of a minor nature were reported upwards through the departmental chain. Local managers were responsible for investigating minor accidents, but in the case of accidents of a more serious nature a formal type of inquiry would be held by a senior railway manager at divisional level, accompanied by technical representatives where necessary. All fatalities, main line derailments and most collisions were dealt with in this manner. All these investigations and inquiries were held in private.

All accidents, except those of a minor nature, were reported to the Railway Inspectorate by Regional Headquarters. Most of them would be either noted or finalised in correspondence, but the most serious ones would be the subject of an inquiry under the 1871 Regulation of Railways Act. These inquiries were invariably held in public, although there was no legal requirement to do so, and a report was always published (which was a legal requirement). Accidents to staff were inquired into by Railway Employment Inspectors, a branch of the Railway Inspectorate.

The police automatically became involved whenever there was a fatality, because it had to prepare a report for the coroner, and it could decide on the evidence whether there had been a criminal offence. In other cases, the BT Police would be notified of any serious accident, even when there had been no fatality.

The whole situation changed when the railways were privatised. In BR days, an investigator could be expected to be impartial, whichever department or individual was at fault. There was no point in acting otherwise. However, under privatisation any company could be involved in an accident, but if it happened on Railtrack's infrastructure it would naturally fall to be investigated by Railtrack. In the case of a derailment several companies could be involved — Railtrack, the Train Operating Company, the Train Leasing Company, etc. If there had been a lot of damage to vehicles, track, signalling and/or the overhead electrification, the cost of repairs or renewals, together with compensation cost for delays, could run into millions. In such circumstances, could Railtrack be relied upon to be absolutely impartial in cases where it might have been at fault itself? Perhaps it could, but the other companies were hardly likely to accept the risk of bias.

The very sensible solution adopted was to appoint a suitable chairman from a list of respected, qualified individuals who had held senior positions in relevant railway disciplines and were experienced in leading accident investigations. The chairman so appointed is assisted by a panel of experts from the railway industry, or any outside bodies able to contribute. The inquiry proceedings are held in private and are not open to the media. This encourages people being interviewed to speak as freely as possible. However, observers from the companies involved, and the railway trade unions, are invited to attend.

So far as public inquiries into main line railway accidents are concerned, these have invariably been held by an Inspecting Officer or Inspector of the Railway Inspectorate from 1840 until the Southall Inquiry, with the exception of the accidents at Tay Bridge in 1897, at Hixon level crossing in 1968, and at Clapham in 1988. The HSE decided to repeal the 1871 Act, with its provision for an Inspector's Public Inquiry, and rely upon the powers contained in the Health & Safety at Work Act 1974. This has no provision for a public inquiry held in the traditional manner by an Inspector of the Railway Inspectorate. On the contrary, it demands a judicial inquiry if the inquiry is to be held in public. We have now seen the result — inquiries which last several months with hundreds of witnesses interviewed by lawyers representing a whole variety of interested parties, at a cost of millions of pounds. The HSE then found itself accused of possibly contributing to an accident by its own failures. This was a new development, arising from the Ladbroke Grove accident, and it was one of the issues to be considered by Lord Cullen —

the arrangements and the organisation responsible for the investigation of accidents.

In reality, there was never any good reason to separate accident investigation from the remainder of HM Railway Inspectorate. It is an integral part of its duties, and it is the only body with the required expertise. The shortcomings in the performance of HMRI at Paddington were exceptional and the consequence of the HSE failing to provide it with the necessary resources of the required calibre. Cullen has put that right. However, almost all the parties at the inquiry also felt strongly that HMRI should not be part of the HSE. Cullen was not prepared to go so far, but he decided that it should be divested of its responsibilities for accident investigation. These, he said, should be the responsibility of a newly formed Railway Accidents Investigation Branch (RAIB).

This introduces new problems. Accident investigation is an integral part of safety regulation, and vice versa. Having them in completely separate public bodies introduces the unnecessary complication of liaison and two-way communication of knowledge and information. There is no certainty that the two bodies will be on good terms and will co-operate readily and willingly with each other, especially if one has publicly criticised the other. Do Cullen's recommendations merely lead to another guest at the banquet when there is a serious accident? Let us examine his precise recommendations on this subject.

There were 13 recommendations, the main ones being:

- The responsibility of the HSE for the investigation of rail accidents should be transferred to an independent body, called, for convenience, the Railway Accidents Investigation Branch.

- The investigation of rail accidents should be brought under the overall control of the RAIB, based on the model used in the aircraft and shipping industries. The RAIB would have a structural and reporting line direct to the Department of Transport.

- The more serious cases should be the subject of inquiry by the RAIB.

- The sole objective . . . should be the prevention of accidents, and it should not be the purpose of an investigation to apportion blame or liability.

- Representatives of those who have been affected by an accident should be allowed to attend *as observers* [author's italics] at an RAIB inquiry into that accident. *[Author's comment — this could be the thin end of the wedge. The RAIB must maintain control and ensure that such people are not allowed to take part in the inquiry. They must not be allowed to speak or ask questions. The presence of injured and bereaved with a range of emotions does not sit well with an impartial and impersonal inquiry process. Witnesses might well feel intimidated and there will inevitably be tension. It is not a good idea.]*

- The reports of RAIB inquiries and formal industry inquiries should be published, subject to the protection of the identity of persons involved.

- There is a need for a protocol dealing with the release of technical information and access to technical experts in investigations involving the police.

[Author's comment — this is one of the most important and contentious recommendations and is dealt with below.]

- The statements made by witnesses in connection with RAIB inquiries and industry inquiries and investigations should not be disclosed to the police, save by order of a judge.
  [Author's comment — this is a well-intentioned proposal to encourage witnesses to speak freely without fear of incriminating themselves, but it remains to be seen how witnesses, and more importantly their legal representatives, will take it on trust. The prohibition on disclosure should equally apply to the HSE.]

There could now be four parties with an interest on site. The RAIB and Railtrack, both with a responsibility to investigate the cause, the HSE as the safety regulator, and BT Police, with a variety of duties but immediate investigation of the cause ought not to be one of them. The latter should not interfere with either RAIB or Railtrack's investigations, but should rely upon the RAIB to keep it advised of the progress of the investigation. The same procedure should apply to the HSE. If that protocol can be followed, site investigations should be straightforward, with the RAIB and Railtrack co-operating with each other, as was the practice between BR and the Railway Inspectorate. However, it will require the BT Police to adopt a less intrusive stance, and it will require the RAIB to take a very robust and positive one, determined to allow no untoward interference. It will need some strong characters in its ranks. But it has to be said that the approach of the new Chief Constable is much more encouraging. There should be no need for HSE to be on site at all — it can obtain all the information it requires from RAIB when its investigation is complete.

Lord Cullen requires the HSC to establish the RAIB, which will also require primary legislation. The Parliamentary Bill was published in January 2003 and is expected to become law later in the year. And just as a matter of interest, Lord Cullen might have been expected to comment on the situation that both the railway companies and individuals can be subject to double prosecution, both by the BT Police and by the HSE, as occurred following the Southall accident. This seems unfair and the antithesis of natural justice.

The HSE has been charged with the responsibility for setting up the RAIB and has issued a consultation document. It recognises that RAIB investigators must have an unfettered right of access to accident sites and evidence, and that the investigation and promulgation of safety-critical conclusions are not delayed by HSE or criminal prosecutions. These are clearly lessons learned from the fiasco of the judicial inquiry and the four prosecutions following the Southall accident. And one is glad to see that the HSE belatedly recognises the need for rail services to be resumed as soon as possible. We might hope that these aims will be included in the primary legislation needed. It proposes quite reasonably that reports of the RAIB should be published.

The HSE also suggests that the HSC should retain the power to hold public inquiries into rail crashes, by which it presumably means arranging a judicial inquiry of the Ladbroke Grove type. The HSC should certainly not have this power. The RAIB is the body established to investigate all railway accidents and must not be subject to any form of interference from the HSE. Only very rarely might there be a case for a judicial inquiry, and a decision to hold one should be taken by the Secretary of State on the advice of the RAIB. The HSE should have no part in the matter, other than to consider in due course whether there has been an offence under the Health & Safety at Work Act.

The consultation document also includes staffing proposals for the RAIB. It proposes a Chief Inspector, a Deputy, two Principal Inspectors, six Inspectors and eight support staff. Not an overly bureaucratic organisation, but one might compare it with the staffing of the Railway Inspectorate in the 1980s. It had a Chief Inspecting Officer, a Deputy, four Inspecting Officers, about 10 Employment Inspectors, and a small support staff. The recruitment of inspectors to the RAIB will need careful planning from the point of view of a viable career structure. Preferably, they should come from the railway industry and HMRI in mid-career, with the option of a transfer back again later.

The pluses and minuses of the Ladbroke Grove Part 2 recommendations

1. The Pluses

- The creation of the Rail Safety and Standards Board, subsuming Railway Safety, to provide a voice for the railway industry on safety matters, and bring together the various railway companies.

- The removal of the responsibility for accident investigation from the HSE to a new organisation — the Railway Accidents Investigation Branch, with unfettered access to an accident site.

- The strengthening of HM Railway Inspectorate with a new chief, a new railway safety directorate and sufficient staff with the necessary qualifications.

2. The Minuses

- The retention of HM Railway Inspectorate within the HSE.

- The retention of the safety case regime.

Still to be resolved

A protocol for relationships and responsibilities on an accident site between Network Rail, the RAIB, the HSE and the BT Police, giving precedence to Network Rail and the RAIB. This is an opportunity to settle this issue sensibly.

Above:
A Class 91 electric locomotive, No 91001, stands at the head of a rake of new Mk 4 coaches on an East Coast main line express at King's Cross in BR days (31 January 1990).
Alex Dasi-Sutton

Right:
A Class 91 electric locomotive emerges from Welwyn South tunnel at the head of the 13.20 from King's Cross to Leeds on 25 March 1989. These trains now form the backbone of the Great North Eastern Railway franchise.
David Percival

Far right:
Inside the driving cab of a Class 91 electric locomotive.
BR

11 Hatfield, 17 October 2000 — the railway in meltdown mode

The nature of the accident

The 12.10pm GNER express passenger train from London King's Cross to Leeds was 13 minutes into its journey on 17 October 2000 and travelling at about 115mph when it became derailed about half a mile south of Hatfield station (about 17 miles from King's Cross). The Class 91 locomotive and the first two coaches remained on the track, but the remaining six coaches, the buffet car and the driving van trailer were all derailed. The buffet car and two coaches fell over on their sides.

The train was composed wholly of Mk 4 stock, introduced into service as part of the electrification of the East Coast main line about 10 years earlier, and constructed to very high standards of structural stability. Unhappily, after the buffet car had overturned it came into contact with one of the overhead electrification masts and part of its roof was torn off, resulting in the deaths of four passengers. That was a cruel twist of fate. There were about 170 passengers and 12 GNER staff on the train.

It was quickly established that the cause of the derailment was a broken rail.

The history of broken rails and derailments

Between 20 and 30 passenger trains are derailed each year from a variety of causes, but many of these occur in the vicinity of stations and at low speed. Derailments on plain line (ie away from points) at high speed are relatively uncommon, and there have been only two fatalities in the last 30 years from derailments of all kinds. In 1981 a passenger train was derailed at Ulleskelf, between York and Leeds, and one passenger was killed. The cause was a broken weld in continuously-welded rail. Two years later a passenger train was derailed at Elgin when a piece of railhead broke off at the end of a rail on a section of track composed of rails connected together at the ends by pairs of fishplates bolted together through holes in the rails. This type of track is known as jointed track. One passenger was killed.

By contrast, rail breaks which do not cause derailments are very common. In the last 20 years they have generally varied between about 600 and 700 a year, with a low point of 543 in 1988, but they rose alarmingly to 937 in 1998/9 and 917 in 1999/2000. The following year they had gone down to 709, which is about the average of the last 10 years. About 40% of all rail breaks occur in lengths of plain track, away from welds and rail ends. Another 25% consist of broken welds.

There are two possible reasons for the alarming increase in broken rails in 1998 and 1999. Railtrack tended to point to the quite considerable increase in the use of the railway network. Train miles increased from 277 million in 1996/7 to 306 million in 1999/2000, but much of the increase is likely to have resulted from the increase in train services operated by short trains composed of diesel multiple-units. It is far more likely that the increase in broken rails resulted from Railtrack's policy of reducing the annual rail renewal programme. This policy was evident from one of Railtrack's early Network Management Statements, which foreshadowed a rail renewal holiday. The rate of renewal proposed in that statement appeared to predict a rail life of 100 years, whereas an average life of 20 years would be nearer the mark.

The Health & Safety Executive appears not to have appreciated the implications of this rail holiday and gave an impression of being caught off-guard when the number of broken rails suddenly went up from 756 in 1997/8 to 937 the following year. The actual rate per million train miles went up from 2.46 to 2.92 and should have caused alarm bells to ring, both at Railtrack and the HSE. The HSE's response was less than adequate, particularly when faced with a 100% increase in rail breaks on Railtrack's Midlands Zone. One might have expected the HSE to demand an instant meeting with Railtrack's senior management to thrash out the whole problem. Had the HSE done this in mid-1999, Hatfield might have been averted.

However, the HSE would not have needed to intervene if Railtrack had managed its affairs effectively. Unfortunately, this whole affair demonstrates the unrealism of the method of privatisation, and Railtrack's enforced reliance on a whole series of contractors. Those who designed this system against all experienced advice, shadowy figures in government employ, ought to be brought to account. It will not happen. But let it be said that *the Hatfield accident was highly likely to have been caused by privatisation.* It is 99% certain that it would not have happened under the British Railways regime, when civil engineers knew intimately the state of their track, and would have imposed a speed restriction if they had had any doubts at all about the condition of the track. This was a regular procedure in the later years of BR, when renewals were often deferred to save money and meet the government's financial targets. What were known as 'condition-of-track speed restrictions' were imposed in order to avoid the risk of derailment.

Serious track damage was caused at Hatfield on 17 October 2000 after the 12.10 GNER express from King's Cross to Leeds became derailed by a broken rail. The last coach and driving van trailer became detached from the remainder of the train, which proceeded for some distance ahead. *Rail magazine/Philip Haigh*

Above:
BR was not immune from derailments caused by faulty permanent way. A broken welded joint in the rail caused this high-speed derailment on the West Coast main line at Bushey, south of Watford, on 16 February 1980. Although there were no fatalities, 19 passengers suffered serious injuries. *Daily Telegraph*

Below:
A broken weld in the rail caused this derailment at Ulleskelf. The last two coaches of the locomotive-hauled 13.50 from York to Liverpool rolled down an embankment into a field on 8 December 1981. One passenger died and eight were seriously injured. *Yorkshire Post Newspapers Ltd*

The cause of the rail-break at Hatfield

Certain phrases which emanate from the railways become household words in no time at all. Only hermits living in remote Scottish glens can fail to have heard of the phrase 'gauge corner cracking'. They might not have known what it meant, but neither did most of the railway industry, both at home and abroad. It is also known as 'head checking' and apparently it is a specific form of a generic mode of failure known as 'rolling contact fatigue'. Put simply, repeated use of the rail causes tiny cracks to appear, which are invisible at first to the naked eye. If these surface cracks are not removed (the normal process is to grind them out), they will grow into the railhead and eventually cause that rail to break. If there are many such cracks in a short length of rail, the rail, when it breaks, can fragment into many separate pieces. This is what happened at Hatfield. But it raises a number of questions. Why wasn't the railhead ground? Why wasn't the dangerous condition of the rail noticed? Why wasn't a speed restriction imposed? And finally, was this an isolated incident or was the situation widespread throughout the network? It should be noted that the age of a rail is no particular guide. The rail at Hatfield was only five years old, and gauge corner cracking was subsequently found in rail only a year old.

The underlying causes

1. Railhead grinding

BR had a rail-grinding programme, using a special rail-grinding train which ran over the track slowly whilst a battery of grinding wheels ground the surface of the rail to wipe away surface cracks before they had time to develop and

An 11-unit Speno rail-grinding train stands in sidings awaiting its next job. *R. E. Ruffell*

cause potential problems. In order to cut costs, BR itself had reduced the amount of work done by the grinding train, and in 1993 and 1994 it had not been used at all. Railtrack brought the machine back into use in 1996, but three more years elapsed before Railtrack began to take railhead condition seriously, following the increase in the number of broken rails previously mentioned. It acquired a new machine and ordered two more. However, in order for grinding to be effective it has to be practised regularly before the tiny surface cracks have time to develop. It is useless doing so once the cracks have become so deep that traces remain after grinding. Railtrack was also beginning to pursue an alternative to grinding, which was to replace any defective rail. However, that required defects in a rail to be identified, and by that time they may have passed the stage at which grinding would be effective.

The answer to the question — how do the cracks start in a steel rail — is a complex technological issue. Steel rails might be thought to be solid and completely rigid, but in fact they are slightly plastic and will bend and flex as the wheels of a train pass over them. This can be observed with the naked eye under certain circumstances. This flexing leads to tiny stresses being set up in the railhead. Secondly, the area of contact between the tread of a wheel and the top of the railhead is relatively small, possibly only half an inch. This sets up stresses between the area under compression from the wheel and the surrounding uncompressed area of railhead.

2. Why was the dangerous condition of the railhead not noticed?

In fact, it was noticed. As far back as January the same year, routine ultrasonic tests of the track in the Hatfield area revealed that the rail which later cracked needed attention. However, it was not ground until September, which was useless because the cracks were already too deep and the act of grinding may have worsened the condition of the rail.

There were two contractors involved in this story. Balfour Beatty had the contract for maintaining the track, whilst the contract for renewing the track had been awarded to Jarvis. Balfour Beatty had discovered the defective rail in January, and Railtrack had then instructed Jarvis to replace the rail in March. However, Railtrack was unable to provide the required track possession to enable the work to be done, and it was finally scheduled to take place in November and December. So, between January, when the defective rail was identified, and October, when the derailment took place, there was a point in time at which a speed restriction should have been imposed. The regular inspections which were carried out should have indicated when that should have been done.

3. Was it an isolated instance, or endemic throughout the network?

Unfortunately, it was feared to be endemic, and that led to meltdown.

Meltdown, panic and over-reaction — on site

There were three parties involved on site following this accident. It was part of Railtrack's responsibility to inquire into the accident and identify the cause. The HSE had a responsibility to satisfy itself that the cause had been correctly identified, and whether an offence had been committed under the Health & Safety at Work Act. The BT Police had its traditional role to play regarding the dead and injured and preparing a report to the coroner. All three parties grossly over-reacted to a completely ludicrous degree. They

Recent accidents have seen unacceptable delays in reopening the tracks, and one of the primary duties of the various regulatory bodies involved will be to ensure that this is given priority in the future. The creation of the Railway Accidents Investigation Branch should help to achieve this, and herald a return to practical realism and common sense. Following this very serious collision between two West Coast main line expresses at Colwich on 19 September 1986 in which two electric locomotives and many coaches were thrown around in a tangle and the infrastructure was extensively damaged, the lines were reopened four days later. It might also be added that the Inspecting Officer who held the public inquiry completed that part of his inquiries in *one* day. *Gary S. Smith*

appeared to have no concept of time, nor concern for the massive inconvenience to millions of passengers by having this vital main line closed for several weeks. They had forgotten one of the essential principles of railway operation, that the line should be reopened as quickly as possible, and that work to restore train services should start as soon as the dead and injured had been dealt with. Or perhaps the HSE people in charge of this investigation were unaware of such concepts and treated Hatfield as they would any industrial accident? Or perhaps they didn't care, and there was no one with sufficient power to make them do so? They were out of control. It was very sad to see the BT Police, for which one has had great respect in the past, behave in such a manner, though as noted in Chapter 14, a more balanced approach is now being shown.

This vital main line was closed for 24 days, a situation quite without parallel in the whole history of railways. It is something that did not even happen in wartime, but we had real railwaymen and real permanent way engineers in those days, backed by a sensible and realistic safety regulator. All that for one train, a casualty list that was tiny compared with some past accidents, and for an accident that happened on a four-track section where some of the tracks were undamaged and unaffected. In Britain's worst peacetime accident, at Harrow & Wealdstone in October 1952 when 28 times as many people were killed and three trains were involved, the slow lines were reopened *the next day.* At Colwich in September 1986, when two expresses crashed head-on, scattering 11 coaches and two locomotives in all directions the lines were reopened in four days, which required not only the removal of rolling stock and locomotives, but the restoration of track, junctions, signalling and the overhead electric line, all of which had been badly damaged. Similar stories could be told over and over again. It is beyond belief that the whole route at Hatfield could remain closed for 24 days.

The Chief Executives of the Train Operating Companies were justifiably incensed. They said that journey times were

Another view showing the tangle of coaches following the collision at Colwich. It seems little short of a miracle that no one was killed in those coaches, although there were many serious injuries. *Times Newspapers Ltd*

extended by 50% to 100% and that the disruption was virtually impossible to deal with. Passengers deserting the railways for the roads during the disruption were subject to greater risk. The result was an enormous loss of business and a huge setback to the growth of passenger numbers which privatisation had produced. The effect on the freight business was calamitous. Passengers will return when the emergency is over, but once freight customers have decided to take their business away it is far more difficult to regain it.

The Chief Executive of Railtrack, Gerald Corbett, offered his resignation but initially it was not accepted by the Railtrack Board. He left Railtrack a month later because he had lost the support of the non-executive directors. Gerald Corbett had a lot of support both inside and outside the industry, partly based on his performance under hostile questioning following the Ladbroke Grove accident, when he took on the role of 'Mr Railway'.

One of the faults of the privatised structure was the difficulty in providing a figurehead who could speak authoritatively on behalf of the railway industry as a whole. Gerald Corbett took on the role *faute de mieux.*

The main culprit in keeping the line closed for so long was the HSE. It acted as though this was a laboratory exercise to

discover the cause of an accident for which there was no apparent cause. It behaved as though there was no urgency to reopen the line. It purports to act on behalf of the travelling public, but its behaviour indicated an attitude of mind bordering on contempt for the tens of thousands of passengers whose journeys were subject to delays and overcrowding each day. Such behaviour had never been seen before. The HSE was completely out of control, and, whilst the train operators complained bitterly, there was no 'Mr Railway' to take up the cudgels on their behalf. Railtrack managers, who should have been applying pressure on the HSE to reopen the line, were, understandably, keeping a low profile, fearful of prosecution by the HSE, or worse, a criminal prosecution by the BT Police.

Meltdown, panic and over-reaction — throughout the network

The awful consequences of Railtrack's lack of knowledge of the state of its assets were soon to be made crystal clear. One of the first questions to be asked following this accident was whether the nature of the rail break was confined to Hatfield or whether the same situation might apply elsewhere and, if so, how widespread it might be Railtrack was in a panic. It just did not know, nor did it have the necessary degree of expertise at its disposal to find out quickly, but having examined the network and having found several hundred cases of rails affected by gauge corner cracking, it had no sensible answer, other than to apply a blanket speed restriction of 20mph in every case, irrespective of the degree of infection.

No case was found which was as severe as Hatfield, and it would have been sensible to have applied a level of speed restriction commensurate with the risk. Unfortunately, Railtrack's expertise did not extend to this degree of finesse, nor did it have the courage to attempt it, with the HSE breathing down its neck. The HSE appeared to have forgotten its own mantra about reducing a level of risk to 'as low as reasonably practicable'. It could have suggested to Railtrack that speed restrictions should be graded according to the severity of gauge corner cracking discovered in each case, but it did not do so. It was afraid to do so. It was still smarting from criticisms of its lack of forceful intervention in the question of the suitability of the signalling between Paddington and Ladbroke Grove, and it was afraid to allow any latitude in case another derailment should follow as a consequence of doing so. Railtrack's response to the accident may have been weak, but so was the HSE's.

As a result, 20mph speed restrictions blossomed like weeds after rain until there were several hundreds, imposed without notice, throughout the length and breadth of Britain. Unfortunately, most of them happened to be on the main trunk routes, because they had the heaviest traffic and the highest speeds. Reducing speed from 125mph or even 100mph to 20mph several times during a journey played havoc with timekeeping and schedules. Traincrew rosters and coaching stock programmes collapsed, leading to further delays. Cancellations led to overcrowding. Train operators attempted to replan the timetable to bring some coherence, but the rapid changes in the pattern of speed restrictions partly nullified their efforts. It was probably one of the worst times to be a

The up 'North Briton' from Edinburgh Waverley to Leeds was derailed near Amble Junction, on the East Coast main line south of Berwick Upon Tweed, on 15 July 1967. The cause was a broken rail-end, a not uncommon occurrence when the railway had thousands of miles of jointed track composed of 60ft lengths of rail. Fortunately, there were no serious injuries. Despite the number of derailed coaches and the track damage evident from this photograph, the line was reopened *two* days later. *Author's collection*

passenger in the whole history of Britain's railways, and far more widespread than anything in wartime.

Both the HSE and Railtrack appear to have overlooked the danger arising from the absurd proliferation of speed restrictions. How would drivers manage to deal with a multiplicity of speed restrictions, especially when the commencing point and length of restriction were amended with little or no notice. Perhaps both parties were quietly saying to themselves that there was no real danger, because even if a driver missed a speed restriction and failed to reduce speed it was highly unlikely that a rail would break as the train passed over it. But that overlooks the extra burden placed upon a driver in having to locate ever-changing and often interlaced speed restrictions as he approached them at speed. Might his concentration on finding that vital emergency warning sign cause him to overlook a caution signal? The lineside signing of emergency and temporary speed restrictions on which the driver was relying for the safety of his train was often less than satisfactory; indeed it was deplorable in some cases. SPADs did happen. Did anyone consider the possibility of such an occurrence?

The Rule Book describes exactly how emergency speed restrictions should be brought to a driver's attention. Signs are

'H' section girders used to support the overhead electric wires are thought to have increased the damage to the buffet car at Hatfield. This example is at Skipton. *Author*

erected at the lineside as follows, listed in the order in which they are seen by a driver:

- An Emergency Indicator is placed 200yd on the approach to a Warning Board;

- A Warning Board is placed at braking distance from a Speed Indicator;

- A Speed Indicator is placed at the start of the section of line over which a speed restriction applies;

- A Termination Indicator is placed at the end of the speed restricted section of line.

The Emergency Indicator is equipped with two brilliant white flashing lights, vertically displayed, which must be working at all times. It tells the driver that there is a Warning Board ahead for an emergency speed restriction.

The Warning Board is equipped with two flashing white lights, horizontally displayed, which must be working at all times. It tells the driver that there is a speed restriction ahead. The Warning Board also carries an indicator showing the speed which applies over that restriction. The indicator must be lit during darkness.

The Speed Indicator tells the driver that it marks the beginning of the speed restriction, and it indicates the

speed over that restriction. It is lit during darkness, unless it is retro-reflective.

The Termination Indicator tells the driver that it marks the end of the speed restriction. It is lit during darkness, unless retro-reflective.

In practice nowadays, all these indicators and boards tend to be retro-reflective, with reliance being placed on the penetrating headlight now provided on all trains.

Portable AWS-type magnets are placed 200yd before an Emergency Indicator and 200yd before a Warning Board.

Notice must be given to all drivers about the imposition of an emergency speed restriction, after which the Emergency Indicator must be withdrawn.

If trains have to pass over an emergency speed restriction before all the lineside equipment is in place, the signaller must tell each driver. The signaller must also tell the driver specially if the restriction is longer than $1\frac{1}{4}$ miles, until drivers are being informed by special notice.

The complexity of the arrangements can now be understood. They place considerable responsibility on civil engineering contractors to ensure that the appropriate lineside indicators are placed in the correct locations, and that the lights are lit at all the required times. But it is the drivers who carry the heaviest burden, and it was several months before the position returned to anything approaching normal. However, it was all done without any accidents and underlines the professionalism of the driving fraternity. Were there any public expressions of gratitude to drivers when the situation returned to something approaching normality? If so, they were well hidden. And did drivers milk the situation with demands for extra pay for the extra responsibilities? No, they just got on with the job. Drivers are, and always have been, the backbone of the railway.

In a nutshell

It would be wrong to say that an accident of this sort was inevitable, but it was always highly likely, given the fragmented nature of the industry. The likelihood was clearly spelt out during the privatisation process but the government's architects ignored all the warnings from professionals. And the Conservative government was desperate to sell off the railways before its term of office ran out. There was no time for considering the detail. Railtrack and its contractors were equally at fault, but they were the victims of the system. Railtrack was short of experienced and qualified permanent way engineers, but initially it saw no need for such staff. It relied upon its contractors, who were now the reservoir of knowledge and experience. However, it was naïve of Railtrack to put its trust implicitly in contractors without any check on the quality of work being undertaken, and of the manner in which the contract was being performed. No organisation should hand out contracts worth many millions without satisfying itself as to the quality of the end-product.

The question now remains as to whether maintenance of the infrastructure by contractors can ever be made wholly safe and satisfactory. After the accident, Railtrack was quick to suggest that it might take maintenance 'in-house', but it soon realised the pitfalls of doing so. In order to establish its own infrastructure maintenance organisation it would have to recruit many thousands of experienced track engineers and that could prove difficult. There would be obvious dangers during the changeover process. Contractors would have to be compensated if contracts were terminated. But at least Railtrack would no longer have to pay contractors' profit margins.

It is a pity that Railtrack did not press its case more thoroughly when the time was ripe. Early enthusiasm for the change has evaporated but the case remains strong. Railtrack's successor Network Rail now has the worst of both worlds; it has to pay contractors and their profit margins, but it has also had to establish quite a large and costly organisation to maintain an oversight on the contractors. A sort of second-guessing. The fact remains that it would be cheaper, more efficient and safer for maintenance to be done in-house. A start could be made in one of the Railtrack Zones, preferably the one in which there was the most enthusiasm for such a change. Perhaps the new Network Rail will reconsider the policy.

Railtrack's panic over-reaction was due entirely to the lack of knowledge and expertise in the top echelons of the organisation. It was wholly predictable. Its actions went much further than was either sensible or necessary, but unfortunately Railtrack had no means of knowing what was either sensible or necessary. Without such knowledge, over-reaction was inevitable, faced with the penal provisions of the Health & Safety at Work Act and a BT Police Force looking for evidence of negligence that might justify a manslaughter charge. Unfortunately, when panic subsided somewhat, and the need for some of the restrictions, or their severity, began to be questioned, the HSE emerged as the obstacle to some relaxation. Railtrack had been responsible for imposing the speed restrictions in the first place, but when it wanted to relax or remove some of them the HSE proved difficult and obstructive, imposing onerous conditions. The reason for this is obvious. The HSE was in the same position as Railtrack in not having sufficient experienced and qualified permanent way engineers to advise it. It played safe. Stubbornness is the result of lack of knowledge. Neither Railtrack nor the HSE had the required knowledge. Unfortunately, the HSE had the power to be obstructive.

It was the nadir of the railway's fortunes, unparalleled in its 175 years' history, and created by the arrogance of those who framed the Privatisation Bill and forced it on to the statute book under its innocuous-sounding title — The Railways Act 1993. We will return to this question in the last chapter.

Reports on the accident by the Health & Safety Executive

With commendable promptitude, the HSE issued its first preliminary report into the causes of the accident on 20 October, three days after the accident. Fortunately, the Health & Safety Commission had appreciated the inappropriateness of full-scale judicial inquiries into railway accidents, given the examples of Southall and Ladbroke Grove, and had adopted the only other course open to it under the Health & Safety at Work Act, of requesting the HSE to investigate and report (under Sec 14[2][a] of the Act). Judicial inquiries take too long and there was some urgency in ascertaining the cause of the Hatfield derailment and its implications for the network. The preliminary report merely gives some factual details of

the accident, notes the probable cause, and sets out the aims of the investigation.

A second interim report, succinctly expressed in 15 pages, was issued on 23 January 2001. It gives full details of the derailment and the permanent way, which between them occupy just over three pages. The report then goes on to consider the rolling stock, despite the fact that it had nothing at all to do with the accident. The HSE was concerned, quite rightly, to see if there were any lessons to be learned in the behaviour of the coaches after the accident. This is normal practice, both for the HSE and the industry. However, the HSE's investigations on site, and the removal of the rolling stock, were unreasonably and unnecessarily prolonged. There was no urgency demonstrated at all in allowing the site to be cleared and normal services to be resumed. Railtrack was understandably in shock, and the train operators, Great North Eastern Railway and West Anglia Great Northern, could only stand powerless on the sidelines. Meanwhile, tens of thousands of passengers were left every day to fume at the unnecessary delays, sometimes of considerable magnitude.

The HSE has now published the recommendations of its independent board's inquiry into the accident. We learn that the HSE cannot publish a full report until a criminal investigation and legal proceedings, if there are any, have been completed. Is there any reason why these should take two years? And what is the purpose of recommendations issued almost two years after an accident? If any remedial measures were necessary, and they were, they should have been taken at once. In fact, Railtrack did take remedial measures without waiting for the HSE's report. It should be stressed that it is the industry, not the HSE, which is responsible for the safety of the railway.

The main recommendations, understandably, deal with track maintenance and the relationship between Railtrack and its contractors, but provide nothing new. The most important question of how to avoid the risks inherent in such an organisation is glossed over. Here was an opportunity for HSE to shine, to take a bold stance, and make a firm recommendation that the new Network Rail should consider taking track maintenance in-house. But it stumbled at the fence. Making innocuous and trivial recommendations is so much easier and safer.

Into this category comes the one about making catering coaches safer to minimise the risk to staff (and, one hopes, to passengers). It so happened that the casualties were in this coach, but that was a freak result of the accident. Catering coaches have not been shown to be unsafe for their occupants in previous accidents. Did those who made these recommendations consider the experience of the last 20 or 30 years? If not, why not?

There is also a quite sensible recommendation to review the design of overhead electrification masts to make them less likely to penetrate derailed coaches which collide with them. However, was any risk assessment or cost-benefit analysis carried out before making this recommendation? Is there an implicit suggestion that existing masts should be replaced? It could be a useful recommendation in new electrification schemes, but unfortunately there is none in prospect, and enthusiasm for electrification has all but disappeared.

Finally, one hopes that the proposed Railway Accidents Investigation Branch will be more professional and experienced than the HSE has been. Rather like the old Railway Inspectorate, perhaps?

12 Road and rail do not mix — road traffic accident on the M62 near Great Heck (Selby)

AT a quarter to five on Wednesday 28 February 2001, the early morning GNER London express drew out of Newcastle Central station at the start of its 268½-mile journey to King's Cross, much of it at 125mph. It was not crowded at that time in the morning but it was booked to make a number of stops *en route*. The driver was fully rested and drove carefully, obeying all speed limits. Several passengers joined at York just before 6.00am, next stop Doncaster. It never got there.

Somewhat earlier, a Land Rover vehicle towing a trailer loaded with another car left a small Lincolnshire town *en route* for a destination in Lancashire. The police reported later that its driver was neither fully rested nor did he observe speed limits on his way to a fatal rendezvous with a train at a bridge on the M62 where it crosses the East Coast main line. Approaching the bridge, the Land Rover veered off the carriageway and down an embankment towards the railway, coming to a stand on the up main line. At this moment, the 04.45 express from Newcastle was about two miles, but only one minute's running time, away, its driver unaware that disaster was just around the next bend. Although the driver of the Land Rover made a telephone call to the emergency services, there was no time to make any arrangements to warn the train driver. The Land Rover driver was still speaking on the telephone when the express crashed into his vehicle and trailer.

The express was an InterCity 225 propelled by a Class 91 locomotive and consisted of a leading Driving Van Trailer (DVT), eight Mk 4 passenger coaches and a buffet car. There were 99 people on the train. The DVT was derailed almost immediately but it continued, substantially upright and in line, for almost half a mile until it reached a set of points leading to some sidings. Rapidly approaching in the opposite direction was a freight train travelling at almost 60mph and carrying over 1,000 tonnes of coal. At its head was a Freightliner Class 66 diesel-electric locomotive.

The express and the coal train met at the points at a closing speed estimated to be in the region of 140mph. The DVT, already derailed, was diverted at the points towards the opposite line into a head-on collision, which resulted in almost complete derailment of the remainder of the train. The speed and force of the impact catapulted most of the coaches into an adjoining field, which is not surprising when one considers that the impact speed was probably the highest in railway history (even higher than Ladbroke Grove) and the coal train travelling at almost 60mph had an enormous momentum. Six passengers and four traincrew members lost their lives, among them the driver, the customer operations leader and the chef of the express and one of the two freight train drivers. No fewer than 76 people were taken to hospital. It was a terrible tragedy, and a particularly cruel blow to GNER, coming so soon after Hatfield and especially as GNER had no responsibility for either.

The driver of the Land Rover was brought to trial on 28 November 2001 to face 10 charges of causing death by dangerous driving. He was found guilty and sentenced to five years' imprisonment.

An East Coast main line express of the type involved in the collision near Great Heck approaches Peterborough from the north in BR InterCity days. These are push-pull train sets and the locomotive is at the rear in the customary manner. *W. A. Sharman*

Above and left:
The wreckage of the 04.45 GNER express from Newcastle to King's Cross on 28 February after it collided with a Land Rover vehicle which had run off the road approaching an overbridge. The train became derailed and ran into head-on collision with a train of loaded coal wagons. *Rail magazine/ Philip Haigh*

What are the risks of a train colliding with a road vehicle (other than at a level crossing)?

The risks might be expected to be nil, but in fact road vehicles leave the road and find themselves trespassing on a railway line. Occasionally the road vehicle driver loses control for whatever reason and crashes through the parapet of a bridge. At other times a road vehicle goes out of control on a road which runs alongside the railway line. Occasionally, vehicles escape on to the railway from adjoining land. According to the HSE, such events happen 20-30 times a year, but actual collisions with trains are much less frequent — only four or five a year, and actual train derailments are even rarer, less than one a year. Fatalities to traincrews and passengers are rarer still. The HSE calculated that a train would hit another train in the Great Heck manner every three of four centuries. In any case, there is little that the railway industry can do. The responsibility lies with the highway authorities.

Cattle on the line can also cause danger to trains. The leading car of the 18.20 from Liverpool Street to Witham was derailed at Hatfield Peverel when it ran into a herd of cows which had strayed on the line on 18 June 1996.
Michael J. Collins

What action is being taken by HSE and the highway authorities?

A working group was set up in May 2001 under an agreement between the Department of Transport etc and the HSC. Its task was to assess and report on 'the risk of road vehicles blocking railway lines', and to develop a set of reasonably practicable options.

At any one time, there are hundreds of thousands of heavy goods vehicles (HGVs) on the motorways, dual carriageway roads and other trunk roads. They cross hundreds of main railway lines where train speeds are high. How much would it be reasonable to spend to ensure that those HGVs do not crash on the railway below? And we must remember that it was not an HGV that caused the crash at Great Heck, but quite a lightweight vehicle. HGVs rarely crash on to the railway, being driven in the main by professional drivers, so perhaps the authorities should concentrate on steps to prevent lighter vehicles escaping on to the railway, which would certainly be more practical and affordable. But it has to be remembered that the land Rover veered off the road before reaching the crash barrier, which extended for 33.5m at full height from the bridge parapet wall, with an additional 9.2m of inclines fence to a concrete terminal. Highway authorities standards require a minimum of 30m,

The railways are currently spending more than half a billion pounds on equipping the network with the Train Protection & Warning System to save the equivalent of two lives a year. That includes the installation of equipment on the approach to buffer stops, despite the fact that the only justification for such a measure appears to be the two lives lost at Cannon Street station in Mk 1 stock in 1990. There have been no other fatalities in buffer stop collisions in the last 30 years. The railways will eventually have to spend upwards of £3 billion to save another two lives a year. On that basis, is it not reasonable to suggest that the highway authorities should spend at least £1 billion to improve safety at the type

of bridges mentioned earlier? No doubt the highway authorities would respond that if such funds were available they would be better spent improving road junctions which are known to be unsatisfactory and where many fatalities occur. And they would be right.

Experience indicates that most road vehicles finding their way on the railway line do so from bridges on relatively minor Class A and other roads or from land adjoining the railway line. There are thousands of such bridges and hundreds of miles of railway line paralleled by relatively quiet roads. To protect the railway against all dangers from road vehicles would cost untold billions. And it is purely a matter of chance as to whether a collision with a train ensues, and at what speed.

A glance at some examples of cases where road vehicles have crashed on to the railway line illustrates the difficulties of taking effective action which is affordable:

- On 28 February 2002 a van failed to take a bend on a minor road and crashed on to the adjacent Lincoln–Sleaford line into the path of a two-car diesel multiple-unit. The van driver was killed and a number of passengers suffered minor injuries.

- On the same day a car almost crashed through the parapet wall of a bridge over the East Coast main line at Berwick.

- On 29 July 1999 a Class 153 diesel railcar crashed into a car which had gone out of control, crossed over a field and on to the railway. There were no injuries to traincrew, or to passengers in the railcar.

- On 17 November 1999 a Stansted Airport–Liverpool Street train ran into a car which had left the road, crashed through a fence and on to the railway line. There were no injuries to traincrew, or to passengers in the train.

Underbridges are also a potential source of danger from being struck by overheight vehicles. It is known as 'bridge bashing' and is very common. In minor cases trains are delayed, but in major strikes there is a danger of the bridge being damaged and the track distorted, with a risk of derailment. This example is on the A465 Hereford to Abergavenny road near Pontrilas on 24 July 1988. *Author*

There will undoubtedly be places where useful and affordable improvements can be made.

The report of the Working Group

The Working Group has now produced a very well argued and realistic report. The Group was composed of representatives from:

- The Institution of Civil Engineers.
- Railway Safety.
- The Highways Agency.
- The Department of Transport, LG&R.
- University College London Centre for Transport Studies.

It was chaired by Alan Cooksey HSE (to 5 October 2001) and by Richard Clifton HSE (from 6 October 2001). Its recommendations were as follows:

- Recommendation 1 requires the DTLR to lead . . . the development of tools and data for use at local level by highway and local professionals to carry out comparative assessments of the risks of road vehicles obstructing the railway at specific sites.

   The tools should be usable for both locally and nationally managed roads, and for locations including road bridges over railways, locations where roads and railways run close together as well as locations where road vehicles can gain access to the railway via adjoining land. They should provide the simplest and fastest possible way to separate low-risk sites from those requiring further assessment.

   Note — the identification of sites requiring further assessment and possible attention will not be easy. Accidents have often occurred at sites which would probably be regarded as low risk.

- Recommendations 2 and 3 deal with the recording and collection of all relevant information of the road and rail aspects of any incident.

- Recommendation 4 identifies the parties responsible for leading programmes of risk assessment work. Where reasonably practicable measures for improvement are

identified, they should normally be implemented within two years of identification.

- Recommendation 5 requires the DTLR to lead, in collaboration with HSE, Network Rail and Highway Authorities, the development of guidance on measures for managing risk at specific locations where roads meet, cross or run close to railways.

It has always been recognised that there is no easy answer to the problem of road vehicles obstructing the railway line, but there are many potentially dangerous locations where action can and should be taken to prevent road vehicles from escaping on to the railway line. It is particularly important to do so where train speeds are high and the train service is frequent.

A report 'Managing the Accidental Obstruction of the Railway by Road Vehicles' has now been published by the Department for Transport. It sets out who is responsible for safety where roads meet, cross or run close to railways, and who should meet the costs of improvements. There is also guidance on how risks should be measured.

HSE's final report into the collision makes a number of interesting observations:

- The electric locomotive was at the rear of the train, but had it been leading, the severity of the collision might have been as catastrophic, or more so, because the locomotive would have absorbed less energy than the DVT (leading vehicle).
- It is unlikely that improved bogie retention would have had any great effect.
- The large fuel tank on the freight locomotive was ruptured, although there was no fire. Consideration was already being given to means of mitigating the effects of such ruptures following the Ladbroke Grove collision.
- Future designs of wagons could be made less aggressive if angular sharp edges are avoided. They caused considerable damage to the coaches. This was also a feature in the collision at Southall in 1997.

Finally, the various highway authorities are already taking action to improve the protection of the railway at the more critical road overbridges.

⓭ High-speed derailment at Potters Bar — the mystery of the points

The nature of the accident

On Friday 10 May 2002 the 12.45 express passenger train left King's Cross at the start of its journey to King's Lynn, Norfolk. It was formed by a Class 365/5 four-car electric multiple-unit (EMU) of the type introduced in the middle 1990s, and was operated by the Train Operating Company West Anglia Great Northern (WAGN). It was fairly lightly loaded with about 140 passengers and was just one of 20,000 passenger trains that day — a perfectly ordinary journey on a perfectly ordinary day.

EMUs accelerate quickly, and the train was soon into its stride, reaching speeds of up to 100mph on the high-speed East Coast main line. The first booked stop was Cambridge, 58 miles away, for which the booked running time was 45 minutes. It sped through New Southgate and Oakleigh Park, in and out of the tunnels, and approached Potters Bar, 12¾ miles from King's Cross, running freely at its maximum speed.

Just south of Potters Bar station there is a set of facing points which are provided to enable trains to be diverted from the down fast line to the down slow line. They were of the former BR standard design which had been in use for 20 years or so. Derailments at facing points are very rare indeed,

Derailment at Potters Bar, 10 May 2002, showing the layout at the time of the accident.

because there are a number of locking mechanisms which ensure that they not only fit snugly but also remain locked in that position when a train is signalled to pass over them. They remain locked until the train has passed safely over them.

However, on 10 May 2002 they did not remain safe as the 12.45 from King's Cross passed over them. Unbelievably, the points moved as the third carriage was passing over them. Its rear bogie became derailed but the carriage remained coupled to the front of the train and it continued forward until brought to rest by the automatic operation of the brakes when the rear coach became detached. The rear carriage was not so fortunate. It slewed sideways and slid along until it became wedged under the station canopy, spanning both the up and down main lines. Fortunately, there was no train approaching on the up main line. The casualty list was surprisingly high — six passengers were killed and 10 were detained in hospital. Whilst the derailed carriage was sliding along it passed over a bridge, sending debris into the road below which, by a cruel stroke of fate, killed a pedestrian.

Until recently, the East Coast main line has had a good safety record but when Christopher Garnett, the head of GNER, heard of this latest mishap he must have thrown up his hands in despair. The GNER service was nicely getting back into its swing following the appalling interruptions to its service at Hatfield in October/November 2000, followed by months of speed restrictions and coupled with floods further north which washed away part of the permanent way. Then, just as the service was getting back to near normal, there

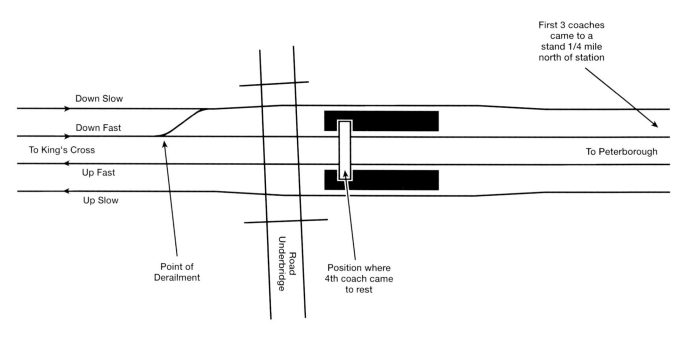

The last coach of the 12.45 EMU from King's Cross to King's Lynn lies wedged beneath the canopies of Potters Bar station, straddling the Up and Down main lines, after its 100mph derailment at facing points approaching the station.
Photograph by Fastline Photographic Ltd

occurred the collision at Great Heck on 28 February 2001. Potters Bar was the third serious accident on the East Coast main line in less than a year and a half. None of these was the fault of either GNER or WAGN; they were the victims. And notably, none of them was caused by a driver passing a signal at Danger. The East Coast main line has a splendid safety record in that respect — no passenger has been killed on that line as a result of a signal being passed at Danger for almost half a century.

The track and signalling

The track through Potters Bar is formed by standard long welded rail on concrete sleepers and the points concerned in the collision were of a modern standard type. Signalling is standard multiple-aspect colour-light, controlled from King's Cross power signalbox.

The two switch blades of a set of points such as those at Potters Bar are connected together by three stretcher bars located at short intervals along the switch blades. The switch blades slide across from one side to another, depending on the route to be taken by the train. This movement is power operated, usually by electric motor. Before the signal in rear can be cleared from red, the points must be detected to be fitting closely to one or other of the stock rails. This detection

is carried out at the points. The points are then locked either electrically or mechanically, after which the signal can be cleared. To prevent any movement of the points as the train approaches, they remain locked as long as track circuits approaching and through the points are occupied by a train. (Track circuits are a device that detects the presence of a train by a weak electric current being passed through one or both of the rails. When the passage of the current is interrupted and short-circuited by the wheels of a train passing over them, the track circuits become 'occupied' and operate electrical control circuits.)

The movement of points in a main line as a train is passing over them is an extremely rare occurrence. There needs to be some special circumstance for this to happen. There was a case many years ago when a rodent gnawed through the insulation covering some wires which allowed a cross-current to flow and operate points as a train was passing over them. Was there some other rare occurrence at Potters Bar on Friday 10 May 2002? It was quickly discovered that indeed there was.

Above:
Class 365 electric multiple-unit No 365525 stands at the down slow platform in Potters Bar station on 1 October 2002. This is the same type of unit as the train which was derailed at Potters Bar on 10 May 2002. These aluminium-bodied units were built at York in 1994/5 and are known as 'Networker Express'. They are capable of 100mph. *Author*

Below:
Looking south from Potters Bar station towards the site of the derailment, where the points from the down slow line to the down fast line have been removed for detailed examination. The bridge deck of the down slow line (at the right-hand side of the photograph) had received superficial damage during the derailment and was renewed in November 2002. *Author*

Above:
A GNER HST speeds south through Potters Bar station on
1 October 2002. HST train sets are regarded by many travellers
as the finest trains which have been built in the last 50 years,
and are a lasting tribute to those who designed them. *Author*

Below:
Potters Bar station, looking north. The last coach of the four-car
unit came to rest broadside across the two tracks between the
platforms, with the ends of the coach wedged underneath the
roof canopies. *Author*

Above:
A Class 365 'Networker Express' speeds south through Potters Bar station on the up fast line on 1 October 2002. *Author*

Below:
HSTs in BR livery. A youthful power car No 43195 approaches Potters Bar station in September 1986. *Author*

Nuts which had been securing one end of two of the stretcher bars were discovered totally unscrewed and lying on the track nearby. How they came to be in that condition is so far a mystery which 50 BT policemen and the might of the HSE, combined, have been unable to discover, but it would have been enough to weaken the points and eventually cause the one remaining stretcher bar to be unable to maintain the forces exerted by a train passing over. How long the points had been in that condition, and why they should fail as the 12.45 from King's Cross, a lightweight train compared with a GNER express, was passing over them, remains a mystery. Meanwhile, the points were cut out of the track and sent away to the Health & Safety laboratories at Sheffield for further examination.

Accidents usually produce red herrings, but some of them may be nearer the truth than is apparent at the moment. It was suggested that the nuts may have been deliberately removed with malicious intent. The CCTV security cameras are said to have shown a number of people in the vicinity of the points that morning. however several commuters are said to have experienced rough riding when passing over the points in previous weeks, and one commuter was so concerned that he reported it when he arrived at Stevenage station in the evening. No doubt the BT Police is following up these reports.

The points are controlled from a relay room at the station and the equipment appears to indicate that they were correctly set for the passage of the 12.45 from King's Cross.

One of the ambitions of the London & North Eastern Railway prewar was to quadruple the tracks in the suburban area from King's Cross, but it could not raise the necessary finance and the project had to wait for the more optimistic early days of the nationalised railway in the 1950s. As part of that project, which involved several new tunnels, a new power signalbox was built at Potters Bar, using OCS (one control switch) equipment. This modern signalbox had a relatively short life and was absorbed into the new King's Cross power signalbox in 1977. *BR*

All signals were at green. So far as can be seen, there was no fault in the signalling equipment, nor in the way in which the train was being driven. It was travelling at well below the maximum speed allowed on the line — 115mph.

A possible explanation

It is understood that, some weeks previously, grinding operations were conducted through these points, an operation that requires the stretcher bars to be disconnected. The question then arises — were the stretcher bars properly replaced and reconnected to the switch blades afterwards? The reports of rough riding mentioned above would seem to indicate that problems had existed at the points for some weeks. And if failure to reconnect the stretcher bars after grinding turns out to be the cause, it demolishes the HSE's rather absurd allegation that there is something inherently wrong with this design of points.

The mystery of the derailment at points at Potters Bar concerns the nuts which should have been securing stretcher bars but had been detached and were lying on the ballast nearby. Stretcher bars maintain the correct distance between each of a pair of point blades. For many years the designed maximum speed at which trains could pass safely through points was limited to 25/30mph. The point blades were quite short and the operating mechanism was simple. When high-speed points were designed, much longer point blades were needed. Not only were additional stretcher bars required, but intermediate drive mechanisms were necessary to avoid distorting the point blades. All facing points (ie points which can change the direction of trains) are provided with safeguards: (1) a lock to prevent the points moving as a train passes over, and (2) detection linked with signals to prove that the point blades are in the correct position and that one blade is fitting closely to the stock rail. Various types of points are illustrated in the following photographs.

Above:
The traditional manner of operating point blades manually from a nearby signalbox is shown here. Between the rails can be seen the facing point lock, and a rod runs at right angles from the tip of each point blade to a detection apparatus. The signals cannot be cleared for a train to pass until the detection has been proved. Three stretcher bars are provided. *LNER*

Below:
Electrically operated facing points at Weaver Junction (West Coast main line). Owing to the length of the point blades two additional drives are provided by cranks and rodding. *BR*

Subsequent developments

Railtrack checked about 800 sets of points across the country for similar faults, but none was found. HSE inspectors also examined points in the Potters Bar area, but found none with loose bolts.

At the end of June 2002 the HSE issued a progress report compiled by an HSE Investigation Board. Despite the passage of seven weeks it had little new to say, and excused this by saying that much of its detailed findings could not be revealed because doing so may impede the ongoing investigation. It also said that it was too early to pronounce definitively on the direct or root cause of the accident, which is being led by the BT Police.

Almost all the witnesses at the Cullen Ladbroke Grove Part 2 Inquiry recommended strongly that the responsibility for accident investigation should be taken away from the HSE and become the responsibility of a new organisation called the Railway Accidents Investigation Branch. It cannot come too soon.

The Investigation Board's report is full of vague, questionable statements. It states that 20% of the points in the Potters Bar area were not fully tight, but in fact the tests by HSE personnel were not carried out in the proper manner. It admits that following a sample inspection of points across the network none was found to be

in the condition of those at Potters Bar. However, it also mentions out that the condition of the points in one area was so bad that HMRI instigated formal enforcement action. In fact, this refers to only a single set of points that was already out of use. Misrepresentations such as these tend to call into question the validity of the whole report.

This is emphasised in its recommendations. It states blandly that: 'Railtrack should review the design arrangements [of points such as those at Potters Bar]'. It goes on to say: 'Railtrack should review the design of such points to see if they can be replaced by a design that is more inherently safe'. Yet in fact the Investigation Board has produced no

Above right:
Electrically operated 'clamp-lock' points at Tisbury Loop, between Salisbury and Exeter. Three stretcher bars are provided, the furthest of which has a drive motion provided by cranks and rodding. *BR*

Right:
Electrically operated points at Euston with two stretcher bars and two drives. *D. C. Hall*

Below and right:
Two views of an electrically operated
set of points with three stretcher bars
and an additional drive.
(Both) Author

evidence to show that there is anything wrong at all with the design of such points, which have been installed all over the network during the past 20 years. So what is the justification for these completely unsubstantiated recommendations? Again, it calls into question the validity of the whole report. It is also full of vague assertions.

Who were the members of this board, and what were their qualifications? There were four members — two from the HSE with specialised expertise and experience, not in permanent way affairs as might be expected, but in Health & Safety regulation. One of them is an expert in the HSE Nuclear Safety Directorate, which does not at first sight appear to have much in common with a set of points at Potters Bar. There were two external members, one who spent all his working life with the British Airports Authority (not many points there) and the other who spent his time in aircraft design and with British Gas (not many points there either). All very eminent people in their own fields, but not what one would have considered a natural choice for an investigation concerning railway points. But it merely follows HSE practice which has been consistently to devalue technical experience and qualifications in railway engineering, and led to so many parties at Lord Cullen's inquiry to recommend that HMRI be completely separated from the HSE. His failure to do so may come to be regarded as a serious error.

The report makes such fatuous statements as: 'Points are one of the engineering safety critical components of the rail network' and 'Others include signals, rails, crossings and wheels'. It states that no evidence had been found to support theories about vandalism or deliberate unauthorised inter-

ference. It leaves unstated the *sequitur* that no evidence had been produced to support any explanation of any sort, but it admits that detailed examination of the points by experts *is continuing*. After seven weeks, how much more examination is possible? Finally, it presumes to makes 14 recommendations, without having discovered any reason for the state of the points. HSE reports are generally factually accurate and well reasoned. This one fails on both counts.

Postscript

There have been two more recent derailments, fortunately not with fatality or serious injury. The first occurred on Sunday 10 November 2002 at Aldwarke Junction, near Rotherham, when a Freightliner coal train was derailed. The previous weekend a section of a facing point — the crossing — had been removed and a short section of plain line installed. Unfortunately the switch blades had not been clipped and scotched (wedged) as they should have been, and the derailment occurred when the points were moved to divert the train away from the straight line. A Railtrack spokesman was reported as saying that the clipping and scotching should have been done by the contractor.

The second derailment occurred a fortnight later on Sunday 24 November 2002, when the leading bogie of the fourth coach of a Great Western Trains HST, the 16.30 from Swansea to Paddington, left the track. The train was travelling at 120mph and carried 450 passengers, but the fates were kind and no one was seriously injured, although it was an alarming experience to those on board. The derailment happened

at Slough East Junction (coincidently the site of the collision in 1997), but the whole train remained upright and in line, and eventually came to a stand near Ealing Broadway. The cause appears to have been a broken fishplate at a bonded joint between two lengths of rail. The break occurred midway along the fishplate. One half remained attached to the rail-end, but the other flew off and became wedged in the 'V' of the points, causing the derailment. It is reported that the two bolts which hold the fishplates on each side of the rail together were found on the ballast. The nuts, which had become unscrewed, were lying on the ballast at the other side of the rail. How they became unscrewed remains to be seen.

Since this accident, Network Rail has announced that it intends to bring infrastructure maintenance for the Reading–Paddington section of route in-house, rather than relying upon contractors. This is intended to give Network Rail experience of direct control of the work.

Above left:
A new type of point being installed on the West Coast main line at Ledburn Junction, 22 October 2002. This is a high-speed junction and the points are known as 'HPSS', a high-performance switch system manufactured by IAD Rail Systems. They have recently been installed at Nunhead Junction and St Mary Cray on the former Southern Region, and at other locations on the West Coast main line. *Author*

Above:
The HPSS points also include a movable 'frog' to provide what is effectively a continuous rail. *Author*

Below:
HPSS point assemblies incorporate their own integral sleepers for greater accuracy in setting and operation. *IAD Rail Systems*

⑭ A verdict on the past. A view on the future

How safe has privatisation been?

In the nationalised British Rail's dying days, during the seven years from 1990 to 1996, there were only eight passenger fatalities in train accidents. On the privatised railway, during the six years from 1997 to 2002, there have been 52 passenger fatalities in train accidents. That, of course, invites an over-simplistic interpretation. The incidence of fatal train accidents over a relatively small number of years fluctuates, and the number of fatalities in any particular accident is a matter of chance. However, if we examine the causes of the fatal train accidents since privatisation, we might then be able to judge whether privatisation has had any effect.

Watford South Junction — 8 August 1996 (Chapter 1)

This is included, because Railtrack had already been created and was being prepared for selling off.

Following an examination of the circumstances of that accident it is apparent that changes which ought to have been made to the signalling were not carried out and the design of the scheme was corrupted in a way that would not have occurred in BR days.

Southall — 19 September 1997 (Chapters 3 and 4)

Whilst one cannot say for certain that the accident would not have happened in BR days, it is very likely that the easier and more reliable arrangements for passing messages that then existed between drivers, signalmen and one control office would have led to effective action being taken that would in turn had avoided the HST running from Swansea to Paddington without the driver having the assistance of AWS. That was the outcome of a privatisation process which placed signal operation in the Railtrack sphere and train operation with the train operators. It was a fundamental error. Signalling and train operation have always, throughout railway history, belonged to one and the same department. If it had not been safe and efficient to do so, it would surely have been changed at some time in the last 150 years. One regrets that Professor Uff apparently did not appreciate this, otherwise his report would surely have had a recommendation accordingly. The opportunity was lost.

Ladbroke Grove — 5 October 1999 (Chapters 5 and 6)

One would like to think that if BR had still existed it would have taken some effective action to improve the signal sighting between Paddington and Ladbroke Grove, and/or to have reduced the number of bi-directional movements or train speeds, but it is not certain that it would have done so. It was initially a BR design, but it was the advent of electrification in Railtrack's days that worsened the drivers' sighting of signals. Railtrack failed to respond effectively to drivers' concerns; they belonged to different companies.

The need for a train operator (Thames Trains) to recruit drivers from outside the railway industry would not have arisen in BR days, because all drivers belonged to the same employer. Everything would have belonged to BR, and any new drivers required would have received the standard training. Whether this would have been enough to avoid the SPAD at signal SN109 can only be a matter for speculation.

There is then the question of the actions of the signalmen. They were heavily criticised by Lord Cullen for failing to react in a sufficiently timely manner to the SPAD. He put it down to a culture. The question of whether that culture would still have existed if BR had been in control (after all, the culture certainly pre-dated privatisation) is a nice one, and there is no certainty that it would have changed.

All in all, however, there are some grounds for believing that a number of beneficial changes would have taken place if BR had still been in control, or that different circumstances would not have arisen, that would have avoided the conditions which existed and led to the SPAD at signal No SN109.

Hatfield — 17 October 2000 (Chapter 11)

One can say with a degree of confidence that this accident would not have occurred in BR days. It is inconceivable that a BR civil engineer would have allowed the track to deteriorate into such a dangerous state without taking some action, at the very least by the imposition of a temporary speed restriction. Railtrack was partly the prisoner of the Railways Act, but it appears to have too readily assumed that contractors would do all that was necessary to maintain the track in a safe condition, without necessarily having sufficient grounds for such optimism. It ignored the warning signs. Without a shadow of doubt, Hatfield was the product of a form of privatisation devised by people who had no experience or knowledge of the nature of track maintenance, and rejected all advice. They were concerned only to sell off the railway before the imminent election. We are accustomed to a degree of cynicism from governments; it is the nature of the system, but this was arrogance on a grand scale.

Potters Bar — 10 May 2002 (Chapter 13)

The cause of this accident is still shrouded in mystery, but suspicion is bound to fall on work undertaken at the points some weeks previously. There may be good reasons why the nuts

were removed, but in the absence of any announcement from the regulatory authority or the police, after the passage of almost a year, one can only speculate. It is becoming increasingly clear that the sooner the Railway Accidents Investigation Branch (RAIB) is established, the better it will be. It is unlikely that experts in the RAIB (and one fervently hopes that it will be staffed by people who know about such things) would have failed to ascertain the cause within a short time.

Has privatisation caused more accidents?

All the accidents discussed above have, in some measure, been caused by the manner and the effects of privatisation. Among the causes of the Southall accident was the divided responsibility for train signalling and train running. The reasoning behind the split is simple — Railtrack was the only system-wide permanent body. It would have been difficult to have given the responsibility for train signalling to a large number of train operating franchisees, but the protocols which Railtrack had to adopt for giving train operators equable treatment could just as easily have applied to a train operator in charge of train signalling. The declared plan of the Strategic Rail Authority is to have fewer franchises, and in particular to have only one franchisee for each main route radiating from London. It would then be simpler to transfer responsibility for train signalling to the train operator. It would be the duty of the Rail Regulator to ensure fair play, but that duty could just as easily be undertaken by a pan-industry body, perhaps an enlarged Railway Industry Safety Board. In principle, the industry should be self-regulating to the maximum possible degree.

The Ladbroke Grove accident had its roots in a number of causes and has been discussed in detail above. Some, or all, of those individual factors were influenced by the organisation created by privatisation. It brought into sharp focus the

A Hull Trains Class 170 diesel multiple-unit speeds through Potters Bar *en route* to King's Cross from Hull on 1 October 2002. Actually Hull Trains is not a franchise, but is one of the very few open-access operators. *Author*

failure of Railtrack to consider itself an engineering company, rather than simply a property company.

The Hatfield accident might be regarded as another Railtrack failure, but privatisation had created an organisation in which all maintenance was to be done by contractors. It might have seemed a neat arrangement to those who designed it, but it was very much a leap in the dark and Railtrack should have taken steps to make sure the new arrangement worked, instead of taking everything on trust. The government assumed that competition for contracts would bring down prices, overlooking the fact that lower prices might affect safety standards.

The verdict?

It would seem from the above that the railways have been less safe since privatisation, but perhaps that is also oversimplistic. It is merely an examination of the causes of five accidents. If privatisation had not taken place, would the long safety honeymoon which the railways experienced between 1990 and 1996 have continued? There are good reasons for accepting that it would. Apart from these five isolated major accidents the railway has been remarkably safe. The latest Railway Safety Report from the HSE, covering the period from 1 April 2001 to 31 March 2002, shows that the number of significant train accidents that year — 56 — was half that recorded in the first half of the 1990s. The statistics may not be entirely accurate, and need close inspection to appreciate the full picture, but they are, none the less, encouraging.

And it would be over-optimistic to suggest that if privatisation had not taken place, no serious isolated accident would have occurred. But the fact remains that privatisation was an underlying factor in the five serious accidents listed above that did occur.

What of the future?

The Strategic Rail Authority

It would be unusual to conclude a book which examines the current railway scene without saying that there are many changes in prospect. It was ever thus. However, the biggest change currently is in the nature of the Strategic Rail Authority (the SRA). It was envisaged as a vehicle for taking a long-term view. It was to be the SRA's view of the desirable railway in 10 or 20 years' time. That would set the industry on course, and it would be up to the industry to fill in the detail of the grand design in order to achieve the desired result. The SRA's most important function would be to obtain and guarantee the necessary long-term funding, whether from private or from public sources.

Apart from the last item, one has to say: 'Not any longer'. Chairman Richard Bowker clearly does not trust the railway industry. He does not believe that it is capable of filling in the detail of the grand design and of implementing it on time and on budget. He may of course be right but it is evident that the fiasco of the West Coast route modernisation has seared his soul and may have influenced his judgement. He has therefore taken unto himself the levers of power and now wields more authority than any previous railway chairman ever did. There is then the obvious danger that that is too much power for one man. His organisation not only determines railway

policy but it does so in detail. His organisation is not of the railway, nor is it of the government. It is a free-standing agent, but with access to capital.

However, there have been successes as well as failures. We have seen whole fleets of new trains. The problem has been, and still is, the inflated cost of modernisation schemes, of what are now referred to as 'enhancements'. Why are costs inflated to such an extent? Why are they up to three times what they would have been in BR days? Some of the answers are known — costs arising from the multiplicity of contractors; compensation payments (the curse of the industry); the use of expensive consultancies; the demands of an obsessive Health & Safety Executive. There is another curse on the industry too — the contracts culture, with all its hidden costs — but there seems little chance of escaping from it at the moment. The chairman of the SRA seems to believe in a railway governed by contracts.

It would be very instructive to compare in detail the costs of the East Coast electrification against those of a similar scheme. Has it ever been done? And if not, why not? One hopes that the SRA is working on this issue at this very moment, because the costs of enhancements must be reduced or they will not take place. That would be a tragedy for the railway, and for the country too. It would render impossible the government's goal of a major increase in the railway's freight carryings. This is the major challenge, and it must be tackled head-on. The SRA must take the lead and do whatever is necessary. It has the power. It must not fail the nation.

The SRA's policy of a single franchisee for each main London terminal has much to commend it. Throughout railway history each main line from London was under one control and the determination of paths and priorities in the timetable was done by a single authority which was very aware of the financial implications of its actions. It would be a natural corollary that it should be done by the resident train operator, with proper safeguards for other train operators might wish to use that route, especially the freight operators. The resident

A pair of GNER East Coast expresses stand at King's Cross on 17 October 2002. GNER is widely considered to have been one of the most successful franchises. *Author*

The modern railway at Reading. A five-car Virgin 'Voyager' enters the station on 17 October 2002 whilst the new LED signal, R53, can be seen to the left of the photograph. *Author*

train operator is the obvious body to determine the timetable, because it is closest to the customer and knows what is required. Its commercial success depends on its judgement. But apparently, that is not the SRA's intention. It appears that *it* will determine the paths and any enhancement, but how it will do so at some distance from the customer is not clear. The train operator will merely be an agent who will deliver the end product. And a short-term agent, too. That is very unsatisfactory, unless the SRA has other undisclosed plans.

There is considerable unease about this accretion of power by the SRA. What the industry needs is longer franchises so that train operators can plan ahead with confidence, otherwise they will merely be service delivery units with little incentive to deliver. Apparently their duties will be to run clean trains on time with courteous staff, which is laudable, but very much an end-product.

Whilst larger franchises are desirable in many ways, some of the successes have come from the smaller franchisees, because they are nearer to the customer and the bottom line. They have more scope for quick reaction and for enterprise. They can more easily judge what is needed for success, and they can more quickly implement and adjust their plans. They are not top-heavy. Those very desirable qualities need to be preserved in any new organisation.

Safety in the future

1. Train protection

The major improvement in safety is taking place currently — the installation of the Train Protection & Warning System. It will be completed by the end of 2003 and will fill the loophole in the Automatic Warning System. There will then be more protection against drivers inadvertently passing signals at Danger. It cannot be stressed too strongly that TPWS would have prevented the Ladbroke Grove disaster.

Beyond TPWS, there is the question of the European Rail Traffic Management System. It is very expensive. It is technically advanced and complex, especially in its higher levels. Its benefits, so far as Britain's railways are concerned, hardly justify its cost. It is a European Commission requirement, but some Continental railway administrations are beginning to question the cost, even though it has more advantages to them in facilitating through working. In Britain it can be justified only when it replaces life-expired signalling on a whole route and it will have to be regarded as a long-term, ongoing plan, taking many years. Its safety benefits are relatively tiny — calculated to be the equivalent of two fatalities avoided per year, plus the unknown factor of the possible avoidance of another major disaster on the scale of Ladbroke Grove.

2. The Railway Accidents Investigation Branch

Lord Cullen's recommendation concerning the creation of a Railway Accidents Investigation Branch (RAIB) is excellent in concept. It places the responsibility for determining the cause of an accident fairly and squarely upon the RAIB, but it must not be overlooked that the railway industry also has that responsibility. The two will have to work together, in exactly the same way as BR and the Railway Inspectorate used to, and as effectively.

The Bill creating the RAIB — entitled 'Railways and Transport Safety Bill' — was published on 14 January 2003. It has the following main features:

- The Chief Inspector of Rail Accidents, and the Inspectors, will be appointed by the Secretary of State.
- The RAIB shall investigate any serious railway accident and may investigate non-serious railway accidents, and shall try to determine the cause. On completion, the RAIB shall report to the Secretary of State.
- There is provision for the RAIB to conduct an investigation and report irrespective of whether or not civil or criminal proceedings are in progress.
- Inspectors will have a range of powers to assist them to conduct their investigations.
- The Chief Inspector may give directions regarding the investigation into accidents by the railway industry.

The powers, duties and responsibilities of the RAIB are commensurate with its function, and in many respects similar to those which existed under the 1871 Regulation of Railways Act. However, as is the common practice, several decisions have been left to the Secretary of State, which will be made by Statutory Instrument after the Bill becomes law. The Bill does not mention the roles of either the HSE or the BT Police in the investigation of railway accidents, nor of the protocol which both parties and the RAIB will need to create and observe. This could well be a contentious issue, and one would hope that the Statutory Instrument will give positive guidance. Lord Cullen recognised this as being a

difficult area, and the primacy of the RAIB in the investigation of accidents needs to be emphasised.

3. The Health & Safety Commission

The Health & Safety Commission and its executive arm, the Health & Safety Executive, are both well-intentioned, but like all single-issue organisations they tend to become over-zealous in their aims, to the point where they lose sight of the need for balance and common sense, for practical realism, in their actions. That is a great pity. There is a need for a safety watchdog, but it needs to be staffed by experts in their particular field. So far as railways are concerned, that means experienced railway operators and qualified engineers with experience of the railway industry, otherwise HM Railway Inspectorate will never gain the trust and confidence of the industry, nor its willing co-operation.

The HSE needs to review its stance. It needs to be less obsessive and more realistic. It is more likely to achieve its aims by working in co-operation with the railway industry than by wielding a big stick. There may be occasions when the latter has to be resorted to, but it should not be necessary if there is trust and respect between the HSE and the railway industry. One of the main problems is that HSE policy is the same across the board, but the railway is not like other industries and needs different treatment. One can only hope that under the new leadership of HM Railway Inspectorate there will be a more intelligent approach. Lord Cullen severely criticised the HSC/HSE with some justification for its inefficient stewardship of the Railway Inspectorate and recommended that a new senior post should be created to take charge of it. The HSE has responded by creating such a post and appointing Alan Osborne to it. He will be a member of the HSE Board, which is an indication that the HSE now regards HMRI as being more important than it had previously recognised. Alan Osborne now needs to rebuild the trust and respect between HMRI and the railway industry which once existed, and replace coercion with co-operation. That will be to everyone's benefit. If he is successful in doing so we may no longer regret that Lord Cullen failed to relieve the HSC/HSE of responsibility for regulating railway safety, as the majority of witnesses at the Ladbroke Grove Inquiry wished.

4. The British Transport Police

The BT Police was criticised by both Professor Uff and Lord Cullen for its over-interventionist actions at both Southall and Ladbroke Grove, and for seriously delaying the reopening of the line. However, there are very welcome signs that those criticisms have been taken to heart, and the BT Police now has a new Chief Constable, Ian Johnston CBE, QPM, who has adopted a much more helpful and progressive role. He is particularly anxious to reduce the delays to trains which occur after fatalities on the line (virtually a daily occurrence) and to enable the line to be reopened more quickly than recently after an accident. These are very welcome developments for the industry and for passengers, and presage a

TPWS grids at a speed trap to provide greater safety. By the end of 2003 the programme to install TPWS will be complete, providing a safer railway. *Author*

Above and below:
Two examples demonstrating the paradox of Britain's privatised railway. New trains are an obvious example of investment. Not so obvious is the infrastructure, which is neither so new nor so shiny, nor has it sufficient capacity to meet the aspirations of the train operating companies. And it has not been safe enough, as the accidents at Hatfield, Potters Bar and elsewhere have demonstrated. In the author's view, only radical change will provide the solution to the present malaise. The two trains shown are (*above*) a Class 460 'Juniper' at Gatwick Airport station on 17 July 2000, and (*below*) a Virgin Trains Class 390 'Pendolino', No 390006, seen at Euston on 30 April 2002. The latter are expected to revolutionise the West Coast main line service. *Brian Morrison*

return to mutual co-operation between the BT Police and the railway industry which until fairly recently was the norm.

Finally, a personal view

Having closely observed the privatised railway as it has stumbled along from crisis to crisis, I have come to the conclusion that the present system can never be made to work without radical change. It is too fragmented and too expensive. Mere tinkering is not the answer, but neither is renationalisation.

Some changes would not be too difficult to achieve. As soon as larger franchises are formed, the responsibility for signalling trains should be transferred to the dominant train operator on each route. That will reunite track and trains, bring increased efficiency and reduced costs, and increased safety. This is a simple prize, greatly to be desired. It will free Network Rail from responsibility for current operations and allow it to concentrate on its core responsibility — the infrastructure. This is another simple prize, and also greatly to be desired.

Following the Hatfield accident and the resulting chaos, there was a feeling that the problem could be resolved only by bringing maintenance of the infrastructure in-house. Initial enthusiasm for such a change has evaporated somewhat, but the justification for it has not. The problem is now one of achieving the change. Network Rail does not want the upheaval, and sees problems in acquiring a sufficient work-

Left:
A West Yorkshire PTE electric multiple-unit stands at Skipton with a train for Bradford on 19 October 2002. These Siemens Class 333 units are closely modelled on the very successful Heathrow Express units and are operated by Arriva Trains. *Author*

Below:
The 17.19 Eurostar train from Waterloo International to Brussels Midi passes St Mary Cray junction. *B. Morrison*

force of suitable quality from the infrastructure maintenance companies (IMCs) which now possess it, but if we want an efficient, safe and affordable infrastructure it will have to be done in-house and be under the direct control of Network Rail. It will cost a lot less by bringing infrastructure costs back under control, and in addition there will be no expensive interface and no IMC profits to pay. Only the will to achieve it is required. The two very recent derailments add an urgency to this matter and just before publication of this book Network Rail made the welcome announcement that it is taking over direct responsibility for infrastructure mainten-ance on the Reading–Paddington section, the scene of one of those derailments. Its stated reason for doing so is to allow

it to obtain experience of doing the work in-house, surely a prelude to an extension of this development.

Infrastructure also includes signalling installations. Rail-track relied too heavily on consultants for all signalling mat-ters, and the new Network Rail needs to have its own experienced signal engineers to oversee the activities of con-sultants, to ensure that the end-product is what the industry wants and can afford. The industry relies far too much on an army of consultants. They are very expensive and often replicate what was done much more cheaply in house in BR days, but have a tendency, common to all consultants, to pro-duce schemes that contain desirable, but expensive, elements as well as the essentials. It is called in the industry 'going over

The GNER franchise has been so successful in attracting more passengers that it has had to supplement its train service with surplus Eurostar sets. One is seen here passing through Potters Bar station at high speed on 1 October 2002. *Author*

the top'. The railway industry should establish its own consultancies and make them freely available to all railway companies. TOCs are generally too small to have consultancies of their own, but the new organisation recommended by Lord Cullen — the Railway Industry Safety Board — should be expanded and take on a wider role, embracing both internal consultancies and Research & Development (see also earlier — Ladbroke Grove Rail Inquiry Part 2).

Then there is the question of vertical integration, virtual or otherwise, of train operators and Network Rail. There was some enthusiasm for this also, but it too seems at the moment to have evaporated with the demise of Railtrack, although there are some powerful people in the TOCs, experienced in running a joined-up railway, who would strongly welcome it. The problem is the nature of the industry — Network Rail is a permanent body; train operators are transient, with lives only as long as their franchise and at the mercy of the SRA which appears to favour short franchises. Integration is impracticable without radical change, so one would need to create a form of regional railway that would own the infrastructure and run the trains on a permanent basis, not as a transient franchise.

ScotRail seemed to favour this approach at one time and it would probably be a popular change in Scotland. Perhaps we should try it. We could also reorganise the industry on a line-of-route basis, recognising that these are its production lines. East Anglia, East Coast main line, Midland main line, West Coast main line and Great Western main line readily lend themselves to this concept. The former Southern Region of BR is a natural candidate. We might then have a properly functioning, efficiently run and affordable railway. And in the midst of all this, freight should be given greater priority in pathing and financing, as it has a much greater potential for growth than passenger traffic. Such a change of emphasis would be popular with both the government and the public.

There are no other realistic solutions to the present dysfunctional and expensive railway. It cannot be made to work efficiently and affordably without radical change, and the sooner that challenge is accepted, the better for all of us. The fact has to be faced that the railway industry is at a crossroads.

The costs of operation must be reduced. If TOCs must be retained, their demands for paths must be more realistic and the path-hungry short train/frequent interval concept, which creates a need for expensive infrastructure enhancements, must be rigorously examined. The costs inherent in employing contractors and consultants must be avoided. Compensation payments must be abolished and contracts minimised. Reintegration is essential. If this is not done, the industry will become unacceptably expensive to run, and enhancements too dear. The government will lose interest in the 'perennial railway problem' and the bright hopes of a few years ago will be extinguished. The choice is stark — radical change or stagnation and decline.

And finally, may I close this book by quoting from the remarks made by Mr Edward Brian Gibbens QC in his report of the public inquiry into the accident at Hixon level crossing on 6 January 1968:

'Safety is a relative concept varying in proportion to its opposite, danger. It is almost impossible to remove absolutely the risk of accident from any form of human activity . . . Safety can, in a sense, be bought like any tangible commodity — the higher the price paid, the better the safety; and, in assessing the degree of safety to be acquired, one must put into the balance, on the one side, the magnitude of the danger to be eliminated and, on the other, the sacrifice in money, time, convenience, material resources (and the neglect of other pressing safety needs elsewhere) in eliminating that danger. There is no such thing as unbounded resources for every desirable reform.'

Those sentiments are as true today as they were then, and should be on every safety regulator's desk.

Index